The Location of British Army Records 1914-1918

Fourth Edition

NORMAN HOLDING

revised and updated by

IAIN SWINNERTON

Published by the
Federation of Family History Societies (Publications) Ltd.,
2-4 Killer Street, Ramsbottom, Bury, Lancashire BL0 9BZ

First edition 1984
Second edition 1987
Third edition 1991
Fourth edition 1999

ISBN 1 86006 084 6

Printed and bound by the Alden Press, Oxford and Northampton

CONTENTS

ACKNOWLEDGEMENTS

A book of this nature is really a compilation of information provided by others. It is therefore to those who have helped by sending me completed questionnaires, lists of books and hints on where to find information on soldiers that much of the credit and my thanks must go. Initially some 350 replies were received from Military Museums, County Record offices, Libraries and individual Family Historians. May I thank them all for the help they have given in the furthering of Family History research.

For the actual reproduction of the text for the first edition I was indebted to Margaret Adams and Linda Bennett who typed what must have been a most boring manuscript.

The need to reprint in 1987 and again in 1991 has given the opportunity to change the arrangement and to make a number of corrections and additions. I am grateful to all those who contributed these. For bringing many of the errors to my notice I must thank Pauline Litton and Pauline Saul. Their careful and accurate proof reading has done much to improve the book. My thanks also to Toni Maundrell and Pauline Saul who did the re-typing and layout.

Norman Holding
1991

FOREWORD TO THE FIRST EDITION

This book is intended to provide those researching the life of a soldier during World War I with a number of pointers on where to look for documents to assist him. It does not include records still held by the Ministry of Defence and the reader is advised to read the author's books on *World War I Army Ancestry* and *More Sources of World War I Army Ancestry,* published by the Federation of Family History Societies, on the methods to be used in the research.

What follows is a catalogue of sources containing lists of men. In very few cases can complete lists of those who served with a Regiment be found but it is hoped that the information given will be of some assistance.

Norman Holding
1984

FOREWORD TO THE THIRD EDITION

There have been few changes and none of the repositories have been contacted again. Several Regimental Museums have written to update their entries and these have been included. Some claimed to have no records, but these often stemmed from a misunderstanding of the phase 'No Records', which was intended to denote 'No lists of men that would be of use to Family Historians'. It was never meant to imply that they held no records of a different nature.

In general there is a growing interest in the men who fought in the Great War, which is one of the reasons why many Museums are compiling lists and indexes from a number of sources. These are frequently incomplete but should not be neglected. The release of the main set of records still held by the Ministry of Defence is not due until 1996 at the earliest but microfilming is already in hand.

The author will be pleased to receive details of any further lists known to readers in addition to amendments to those sources given. It should be noted also that both books mentioned in the Foreword of 1984 recently went into their second editions.

Norman Holding
1991

5

FOREWORD TO THE FOURTH EDITION

The transfer of the WWI soldiers' documents to the PRO in 1996 and of the officers' documents in 1998 (see next page) has necessitated a major revision. The author was fully committed to revising his other two books dealing with World War I soldiers and so asked me to undertake the task. Whilst doing so, I took the opportunity to contact all the regimental museums again and asked them to confirm or update their entries. I have added to the list of useful books several excellent publications which have appeared since the last edition and I have also added the name and address of all the museums, even if they have said they have no records of individuals, I am sure that any family historian worth his salt will wish to visit the museum of his ancestor's regiment to get that background information and 'feel' for the regiment which is so essential to add interest to family trees.

The titles of the regiments used throughout are those in use in August 1914.

Iain Swinnerton
1999

6

SERVICE RECORDS OF WORLD WAR I SOLDIERS

Microfilm copies of service records for other ranks whose service ended between 1914 and 1920 have now been transferred from the custody of the Ministry of Defence to the Public Record Office, Kew. **The actual documents, however, remain at the MoD Depot at Hayes.**

The records were originally kept so that the War office (as it then was) could answer queries about pensions, medals and allowances for disablement. During the last war, unfortunately, about 60% of them were destroyed in the bombing in 1940. Most of those that survived were badly damaged either by fire or from the water that was used to put out the flames. They have become known as the *Burnt Collection* and contain the service records of roughly 25–30% of the estimated 3 million men who served in the British Army in the Great War. They are stored in a staggering 3,000 boxes on nearly 2 miles of shelving but are in such a fragile condition that **they will never be open to public inspection.**

The PRO has received a grant from the Lottery Fund to finance a project to conserve and microfilm them. At my suggestion, in the interest of fairness, filming started at the letter Z. Happily, the PRO are not waiting until the completion of the project to make the records available but are issuing them **on microfilm** as each film is completed. They are classified as WO363. At the time of going to press, the letters ?, N, O, Q, U, V and Z have been filmed and are available for inspection. Approximate dates being forecast for the remainder are:

A,B,C,D – Summer 1999 P – Autumn 2000 I,J – Spring 2002 F – Autumn 1998
? – Autumn 1999   M – Spring 2001   H – Winter 2002 W – Spring 1999
?,S – Spring 2000   K,L – Autumn 2001 G – Summer 2003

Readers should be warned that in many cases, only fragments of pages have survived.

For a fee of £20 the Ministry of Defence will search the records still at Hayes for names beginning with letters that have not yet been released and the search can now be done for anyone, not just the next-of-kin as previously. Write to MoD CS(RM)2, Bourne Avenue, Hayes, Middlesex UB3 1RF.

There is another collection of records known as the *Unburnt Collection* which are already available for searching. These were compiled from duplicate records held by the Ministry of Pensions and comprise the records of another 8–10% (about 750,000) of the soldiers. These have been microfilmed by the Genealogical Society of Utah and were released for public consumption at a special conference held at the PRO on Armistice Day 1996. They are on over 4500 reels of microfilm and are available for viewing in the Microfilm Reading Room at the Public Record office, Kew. It is hoped to have copies of these in other locations in due course and they are, of course, available through LDS Family History Libraries. They have been classified as WO364.

7

Both the Burnt and Unburnt Collections include service records not only for regular soldiers (which can date back to the 1880s) but also for members of the Territorial Force and Special Reserve who had enlisted pre-war and for members of the Royal Flying Corps.

Iain Swinnerton

1

LISTS OF MEN

Any Family Historian aims to find his ancestor in a list, be it a parish register or a census. With 1914 Army ancestors, the lists are few and in most cases too short. The lists can be considered in two groups. Firstly, those dealing with the man as a soldier, which often associates him with his unit, be it Regiment or Corps. Secondly, those drawn up by civil bodies and these usually group him with his peace-time associates albeit that his military details may still be given.

Military lists

List of war dead

Soldiers Died in the Great War 1914–18, HMSO, 1920, 80 volumes; does not give the precise place of death. A copy of the list has been made available on microfilm in the Microfilm Room at the Public Record Office, Kew. The index to Regiments is to be found in a folder on top of the microfilm storage cabinets. See also the indexes and records in the Family Records Centre. It is now also available on a computer CD-ROM disk from Naval & Military Press, PO Box 61, Dallington, Heathfield, East Sussex TN21 9ZS.

Royal Naval Division Roll of Honour. *Soldiers Died in the Great War* omits those who fought in the Royal Naval Division. These are now to be published by the Imperial War Museum in 10 volumes.

List of war dead in the care of the Commonwealth War Graves Commission

Frequently details next of kin, and the location of the grave, if any, gives a clue as to where he was killed. This in turn may help to identify a precise unit which was in that area at that date. Beware of 'died of wounds' entries as he may have died many miles from the front. A small charge is now made to search the records for you. It is now available on the Internet at www.cwgc.org.

Lists of dead

In the care of the Regiment or Corps (Roll of Honour); may give a precise location at the time of death.

Lists of wounded

In the case of the Regiment or Corps only a few exist but when they do, they provide the vital proof that may not exist elsewhere.

'Official' casualty list as it appears in local or national newspapers

In the early days of the war these daily lists gave details of the Regiment but by 1916 even this information was deleted in order to prevent the Germans obtaining too much assistance. Although issued regularly by the Assistant Adjutant General's office they were not always published by the papers, at least not in their entirety. 'Local' names were extracted and published by the local newspapers. Officers' names appeared after about three weeks, men's names took somewhat longer, about six weeks.

From August 7th 1917 the daily lists were combined into a weekly list which consisted of six or seven daily lists. A complete set of these War Office Weekly Casualty Lists can be found in the Newspaper Library, Colindale and the Library of Scotland, Edinburgh, The whereabouts of the pre-August 1917 'Daily List' is not known.

Medal Rolls at the PRO, Kew (WO329)

These are now available for public search. The indexes are on microfiche held in the Microfilm Room. There is one alphabetical list giving all holders of the 1914 Star, 1914–15 Star, British War Medal, Victory Medal, Territorial Force Medal and Silver War Badge (given to those discharged wounded or for other reasons). See PRO Leaflet No. 101 *Service Medal and Award Rolls: War of 1914-18.*

Separate indexes cover the Gallantry Awards: DCM, MSM, MM and Mentioned in Dispatches. The latter has three indexes; all must be searched. Entries in these indexes refer to the *London Gazette,* copies of which are also at the PRO, Kew in Class ZJ1/. . . Very few citations survive. See PRO Leaflet No.105 *First World War: Indexes to Medal Entitlement.*

War diaries (WO95 and 154)

Almost every unit kept a War Diary but these very seldom mentioned men's names. Women nurses were nearly always recorded as they arrived or left the unit. Many Base Hospitals listed men who died, particularly officers (deaths in Base Hospitals were infrequent).

Medical records

The small sample of records remaining in the PRO Kew are in MN106 (Bibl.Ref. 15).

Regiment, battalion or unit nominal rolls

From printed books (see below) and Regimental Museums or CROs. Very few now extant. A few units have embarkation rolls of all those who sailed for France, others have lists of men compiled for special purposes such as the issue of items of clothing, leave or rifle practice, company employment books, Minor Offence Reports, Rail Warrant counterfoils.

Printed books

Regimental histories
Frequently list awards and/or those killed; seldom all those who served. Battalion or unit histories on the other hand often have complete lists as the number of men per unit was much smaller but the books are rarer. For example, one book on a Yeomanry Regiment has no complete roll but includes the 'runners and riders' at the Regimental horse race.

Records still in regimental care
Confined to the Guards Regiments and the Household Cavalry. A very few regiments have 'unofficial' lists or card indexes compiled from many sources which may or may not be complete. Similar lists are held by a few private individuals. The officer training units, The Honourable Artillery Company and the Artists Rifles, have records of the trainees who passed through the unit.

Town lists
Some towns formed 'Local' or 'Pals' Battalions. The men who volunteered for service in these Battalions are usually all listed in the printed books published by the town.

Recruiting books
Exist for a large area of Surrey but are probably not complete (Surrey CRO, Kingston-upon-Thames). There are also a very few still with the Regiment (Bibl.Ref. 15).

Private diaries
Many soldiers kept diaries, which frequently name the writer's friends. (Regimental Museum, CRO, local library, IWM, The Liddle Archive, Brotherton Library of Leeds University.)

Private autograph books
A valuable source of names but, as the books are still in private hands, they are difficult to find.

Field pocket books
Officers carried a small note book. Some of them have survived and list names of men killed as well as men under the officer's command. (CROs, Regimental Museums, private hands.)

County Territorial Force Association
The organisation which controlled the Territorial Battalions of the County Regiment, also the Yeomanry Regiments and the Volunteer Training Corps. Minute Books and Accounts, often in the CRO, sometimes include lists of men.

Regimental and other Associations

May have details of past members. The British Limbless Ex-servicemen's Association has a file on many of its old members, which can give dates of enlistment and discharge as well as Regiment. The Royal British Legion has no central records but some local branches still have lists of past members.

Civil lists

Church magazines

Frequently published lists of parishioners in the forces. (CRO, local library, the Church.)

Church Orders of Service

Service sheets on 'Days of Prayer' frequently listed men.

Village, town and church war memorial unveiling

Order of Service sheets frequently listed those names on the Memorial plus all who served although they might not be named on the Memorial (Fig. 1).

National inventory of war memorials

This is a national project administered by the Imperial War Museum to record the location and other details of all War Memorials in the United Kingdom (including Channel Islands and the Isle of Man). Although names are not being comprehensively indexed they are being recorded for each memorial and a search can be made of a specific memorial if requested.

Write to the NIWM Co-ordinator, IWM, Lambeth Road, London SE1 6HZ, enclosing a stamped, addressed envelope or 3 International Reply Coupons. The Co-ordinator will also be pleased to send details of how you can help with the project.

See also The National Inventory of War Memorials by Catherine Moriarty, *Family Tree Magazine,* Vol.7, No.1, Nov. 1990.

War memorial committees

Formed to erect a memorial to the dead and/or all who served from a village, parish or town. Papers often list names of the men (CRO).

Records of Local Military Service Tribunals

The tribunals dealt with those who applied for exemption from the 1916 Conscription Act. Their records often contain family details but no military information as the man was not yet in the army. Papers may be in CRO or see report in the local newspaper. Tribunals were held within Poor Law Union areas, Urban Districts and Borough Councils.

Unveiling of a . . .
War Memorial Tablet
in the Parish Church,
Sunday, 14th Nov., 1920,

AT 3 O'CLOCK,

— BY —

General, the Right Honourable Lord Horne, G.C.B.

TO THE GLORY OF GOD
AND IN MEMORY OF THE
MEN CONNECTED WITH THE
PARISH OF SHEPHALL WHO
GAVE THEIR LIVES FOR THEIR
KING AND COUNTRY IN THE
GREAT WAR 1914-1918.

DAVID IRAD BRADSHAW
DAVID BYGRAVE
ROBERT CHRISTIAN
GEORGE FREEMAN
JOHN MYERS.

ALEXANDER MACRAE, M.A., *Rector.*

COLONEL H. C. M. WOODS, } *Churchwardens.*
FRED. BROWNING,

D. I. BRADSHAW, Beds Rgt.—Killed 9th Oct., 1917.
V. B. BROWNING, Machine Gun Corps.
D. BYGRAVE, Gloucester Rgt.—Twice wounded, died of gas poisoning, 10th Oct. 1917.
W. CARTER, L/Cpl. R.F.
W. C. CARTER, Mercantile Marine.
V. A. CASTLE, Sgt. R.G.A.
R. W. T. CHRISTIAN, Sgt. R.F.A.—Died Nov. 1916.
W. COTTERELL, R.F.A.
P. C. COX, Machine Gun Corps.—Wounded 12th April, 1918.
G. W. COX, Sgt. Lancs. Rgt.—Wounded 31st July, 1917.
H COX, A.S.C.
J. W. COX, Northumberland Fusiliers.
R. C. DUNHAM, Sgt. Machine Gun Corps.
C. E. FALDER, Hampshire Rgt.—Wounded 10th July, 1918.
E. J. FALDER, Royal Flying Corps.
H. FALDER, R.F.A.—Wounded 3rd. Nov., 1917.
G. FREEMAN, Suffolk Rgt.—Killed 9th Nov., 1917.
F. S. GATES, R.F.A.
G. F. GATES, Hampshire Rgt.
H. GATES, Motor Transport.
J. A. GATES, A.S.C.
S. GATES, Sgt. West Yorks Rgt.—Wounded and gassed. 21st April, 1918.
W. GATES, R.F.A.—Died 8th Oct, 1918. (Name recorded on Stevenage War Memorial).
W. G. GOODSHIP, Beds Rgt.—Wounded 22nd Dec., 1917.
C. A. GRAY, Herts Yeomanry.
J. GRAY, Royal Fusiliers.
J. GREEN, Royal Fusiliers.
W. G. JOHNSTON, D.C.M. Machine Gun Corps.—Wounded 28th March, 1918.
H. V. LEEPUKE, 2/Lieut. Yorks Rgt.
T. A. MOSS, M.M., Beds Rgt.—Wounded 3rd Aug. 1917.
W. MUMFORD, Surrey Rgt.
J. MYERS, Beds Rgt.—Killed 4th May, 1916.
W. J. MYERS, A.S.C.
C. PARRY, D.C.M., M.M., Co. Sgt/Maj. Suffolk Rgt.—Wounded.
C. PHIPPS, R.A.M.C.
E. C. SPICER, R.A.M.C.
H. A. SPICER, Beds Rgt.
W. J. SPICER, Herts Yeomanry—Wounded 2nd Sept. 1917.
W. G. STRATFORD, Sherwood Foresters.
W. J. WINSOR, Sussex Rgt.
J. WINSOR, Machine Gun Corps.
C. O. WILMOTT, Bomur, R.G.A.—Wounded 25th Oct. 1917, and 2nd Sept, 1918.
A. WILMOTT, Queen's Own Rgt.—Wounded 9th July, 1916.
W. WILMOTT, Beds Rgt

Fig.1. Part of the Order of Service for the unveiling of one of the thousands of Memorials. The square on the left shows the inscription on the Memorial; five names without Regiment, Rank or Number. The right-hand side shows the list of all those from the village who served with at least the name of the Regiment. Note the details of the wounded. It is always worth trying to trace such a document. (Order of Service supplied by Mary Spicer and reproduced by kind permission of the Rev. N. Bury.)

Records of Appeals Tribunals

Appeals to Military Service Tribunals were held on a county basis. Proceedings may be closed for 100 years, but check for report in local press.

War Distress Welfare Committees

Organised by towns, villages and parishes to help war widows and wives, children of soldiers etc. Correspondence and minute books in CRO.

War Pension Committees, Soldiers & Sailors Families Association (SSAFA), Soldiers, Sailors Help Society

Records at CRO.

Welcome Home Committee

Papers often include lists of men. Records at CRO.

1915 National Registration

A census to find possible recruits as well as war munitions workers. Believed to have been destroyed. Check CROs but none have reported having lists. Some CROs have associated papers (e.g. Ipswich CRO).

POW Fund Committee

Gives lists of prisoners. (CRO)

Voters' lists

The Electoral Roll for an army camp will include members of the permanent staff. Trainees and other transient personnel had no residence qualification for pre-1918 Rolls. This was abolished in 1918 and hence a larger number of men were included. No army rank or number was given. (CRO, local library)

Absentee Voters' list

For 1918 and 1919 only, gives full details of rank, number and unit. There is no complete collection of these lists. The British Library has only a partial set. Records at CRO or local library. (Bibl.Ref. 15)

Roll of Honour

Many firms issued lists of men serving, as did towns and villages. The local library and CRO may have some but many are still in private hands (Fig. 2).

Local newspapers

Besides the casualty list of local men, sometimes the Nominal Roll of the local battalion was printed prior to it going overseas.

School log books

Some school log books give names of ex-pupils who were serving complete with unit details. May still be at the school, with an old headmaster, the local library or the CRO.

Fig. 2. An example of a Firm's Roll of Honour. This one lists all who enlisted, at least up to 1914. These lists were on pre-printed scrolls sold for the purpose and were mostly completed in the early days of the war. This one may have been completely drawn to order. Many have survived but may still be in private hands. (Reproduced with the permission of Mr. C. Barrett, the son of Barrett B.H., the eleventh on the list.)

2

USEFUL RECORDS IN THE PUBLIC RECORD OFFICE, KEW

Those marked * contain names of men or women.

* Medical Records	MH106/1 et seq
War Establishments	WO24/900 et seq
Army Council Instructions	WO293/1 et seq
Draft of Official Histories	CAB44; CAB45
Embarkation Dates	WO162/7; WO33/763; WO25/3535 et seq
* Women Motor Drivers	WO162/62
Monthly Returns	WO73/97-111
Allocation Tables	WO95/5494
ASC History	WO161/12–13; WO161/30; WO95/5466
* War Diaries	WO95/1 et seq
Orders of Battle	WO95/5467-70
Orders of Battle — Russia	WO33/911
Orders of Battle — Home Divisions	WO33/795
War Maps	WO153/...
Weekly Returns UK	WO114/25-56
UK Units 1914 TF	WO158/927-932
* Part Nominal Roll QMAAC	WO162/16
List of ACIs re Volunteer Training Corps (extracts from WO293/...)	WO161/109
Army Pay Corps Precedent Book (lists small training schools)	WO113/6
* Army Discharge Papers 1900–1913	WO97/5139
* Royal Ordnance Corps Orders (Some lists of men)	WO111/13
Lists of units in named battles	WO161/103

GHQ papers approx. 20,000 files on every aspect of Army organisation (very few names)	WO32/...
Lists of nurses arriving in France are given in:- War Diary of Deputy Director of Medical Services (DDMS) of Line of Communications: see PRO leaflet No. 120 Military Nurses and Nursing Services: Record Sources in the PRO.	WO95/3982
* Lists of Nurses 1903–26. Qualifications	WOI25/3956
Pensions.	PMG34/1–5
Pensions.	PMG42/1–12
* London, Brighton and South Coast Railway Roll of Service	RAIL 414/761
* List of Sailors who served in Armoured Cars in Russia (1915–17)	ADM 116/1717
Correspondence re POWs (not many names)	CO754/...; CO755/...; FO383/..., WO165/39; WO222/...; WO224/...

Medical History 1914–49 WO222/...

* Medal Rolls. See PRO Leaflets Nos. 101 and 105. *Service Medal and Award Rolls: War of 1914–18. First World War: Indexes to Medal Entitlement*	WO329/...
* Service Records of Soldiers 1914–20	WO363/...; WO364/...

* Microfilm and CD-Rom of *Soldiers Died in the Great War 1914–18*

War Diaries of Royal Naval Division. See PRO Leaflet No.49 *Operational Records of the Royal Navy in the Great War, 1914–19.*	WO95/...; ADM137/...

3

BIBLIOGRAPHY

Books useful in finding records

1 *Record Office Report 1982,* John Rayment and Bill Taylor, FFHS.
2 *Britain's Regimental Museums,* Roy Batten, 199 Chiswick Village, London W4 3DG.
3 *A Guide to Military Museums,* Terence and Shirley Wise. 8th (revised) edition, 1994, Athena Books, Doncaster.
4 *British Archives and Sources for History of the World War,* H. Hall, Oxford University Press, 1925. Reference Room Shelf, PRO, Kew. This contains an appendix listing the results of a survey on CROs in 1922. The original report is also in the PRO. Reference unknown.
5 *The Two World Wars. A Guide to Manuscript Collections in the UK,* S.L. Mayer and W.J. Koenig Bowker, 1976. A survey of CROs and other repositories in 1975. Reference Room Shelf PRO Kew, Book 25, Press 13.
6 *A Bibliography Guide to the Two World Wars. An Annotated Survey of English Language Reference Materials,* Guy M. Bayless, Bowker, 1977.
7 *A Subject Bibliography of the First World War,* A.G.S. Enser, Andre Deutsch. Lists books by subject, town name, battle, unit and type of unit. Use with care; some entries have been found which do not appear to match the subject heading.
8 *A Bibliography of Regimental Histories of the British Army,* A.S. White. Covers all periods before and after 1914–18. Does not include memoirs and similar books. There are a few Rolls of Honour.
9 *British Military Museums and Events in the Silver Jubilee Year,* English Tourist Board.
10 *British Union Catalogue of Periodicals,* James D. Stewart and others, Butterworth Scientific Publications, 1956; available from most large Reference Libraries. Several supplements.
   A Guide to the whereabouts of Regimental Magazines and Journals. Look first under 'Great Britain – Army' followed by 'Corps' or 'Regiment'. This will refer you to the actual title of the journal. Also gives repositories which hold a complete set of each periodical.
11 British (Museum) Library Printed Book Catalogue published at intervals. Each of the many supplements has to be checked. WWI appears as 'European War'. The

date of publication of a book does not determine the edition of the catalogue in which it appears. It depends on when a copy reached the Library.

12 *A Guide to the Sources of British Military History,* Robin Higham (Ed.), Routledge & Kegan Paul.

13 *Official Histories; Essays and Bibliographies from around the World,* Robin Higham (Ed.), Kansas State University Library, Kansas, 1970.

14 *World War I Army Ancestry,* Norman Holding, FFHS, 3rd edn, 1997.

15 *More Sources for World War I Army Ancestry,* Norman Holding, FFHS, 3rd edn, 1998.

16 *Take Me Back to Dear Old Blighty,* Robert Southall. WWI through the eyes of Heraldic China Manufacturers (e.g. Goss).

17 *Dictionary of Military Abbreviations,* B.K.C. Scott, Tamarisk Books, Hastings, 1982.

18 *Lineage Book of the British Land Forces 1660–1978,* J.B.M. Frederick, Vols. 1 and 2, Microform Academic Publishers.

19 *The Official History of the Great War. Military Operations: France and Belgium.* This series of some 14 volumes is being reprinted by Shearer Publications, 6 Rosehill Avenue, Horsell, Woking, Surrey, GU21 4SE. Two volumes have been issued. The series is also being re-published by the IWM.

20 *Order of Battle of Divisions,* Major A.F. Becke. Is being republished by Roy Westlake, 140 Wyld Way, Wembley, Middlesex, MA9 6PU

21 *The Territorial Force 1914,* Ray Westlake, 1988. Shows all units of the Territorial Force at the start of the war.

22 *The Times Diary and Index of the War 1914–18.*

23 *Principal Events 1914–18,* HMSO. Reprinted 1988, London Stamp Exchange Ltd.

24 *Chronology of the Great War 1914–18,* Major-General Lord Edward Gleichen (Ed.), Vol. 1 1914–15, Vol. 2 1916–17, Vol.3 1918–19. Reprinted 1988 as one volume.

25 *Monuments of War,* Colin McIntyre, Robert Hale, 1990. How to read a War Memorial.

26 *Trench Maps: A Collector's Guide,* Peter Chasseaud, Vol. 1 British Regular Series 1:10,000.

27 *The World War One Source Book,* Phillip J. Haythornwaite, Arms and Armour Press, 1994.

28 *British Regiments at Gallipoli,* Ray Westlake, Leo Cooper, 1996

29 *British Battalions on the Somme,* Ray Westlake, Leo Cooper, 1994

30 *Locations of British Cavalry, Infantry and Machine Gun Units 1914–1924,* Robert W.Gould, Heraldene Ltd., 1877

31 *Army Service Records of the First World War,* Fowler, Spencer and Tamblin. PRO.

32 *British Regiments 1914–18,* Brig. E.A. James OBE, TD, Naval and Military Press, 1993

4

REFERENCE SECTION

This section contains details of various sources that have been brought to the authors' attention. **It is NOT a complete list.** There are undoubtedly many more but it is hoped that those given will act as a guide to the type of document that can be found by those prepared to search.

Information has been obtained from many sources but mainly from two questionnaires sent to Military Museums and County Record offices. Further help was obtained from family history societies.

Research methods

The method of research is covered in Norman Holding's other books (Bibl. Refs. 14 and 15) and in articles in *Family Tree Magazine*, Vol. 2, No. 6 and Vol. 3, No. 1 (Sep/Oct and Nov 1986). Some problems are highlighted in an article in the same journal Vol. 7, No. 6 (April 1991).

Terms and abbreviations used in the text of this book

Bibl.Ref.	Refers to the Bibliographical Reference.
BL	The British Library, Euston Road London.
Bn(s).	Battalion(s).
Coy.	Company.
CRO	County Record Office, as listed by John Rayment, 1983 edn. (Bibl.Ref. 1).
Div.	Division, a unit of approximately 18,000 men.
FFHS	Federation of Family History Societies.
FHSs	Family History Societies.
HMSO	Her Majesty's Stationery Office (Government Bookshops).
HQ	Headquarters.
IWM	Imperial War Museum (Library of).
Library	Only those listed by John Rayment and a few recommended from other sources have been included. The documents referred to are usually in the Reference Library, Local History Library or Local Archives Section.
NAM	National Army Museum.
NCO	Non-commissioned officer, e.g. Sergeant or Corporal.

'No Lists ⎫ means no lists are kept other than those of men killed. The repository
of men ⎬ may have other records of a more general nature but these do not as a
held ⎭ rule include a list of names.
PRO   Public Record Office.
SOG   Society of Genealogists' Library, London.
TF/TA   Territorial Force/Territorial Army.

Location of sources

Military museums

Enquiries requested details of lists of men both printed and manuscript. Lists of
those killed were specifically excluded as these are held by most regiments; this
information can most easily be obtained from *Soldiers Died in the Great War*. Most
of the printed regimental histories have been located from replies from the museums
but copies are also usually held in the local library, and the IWM Library. These
books normally only list those killed or given awards. Complete lists are sometimes
found in the rarer books on the smaller units, i.e. battalions, artillery batteries and
corps companies. A few museums have some Nominal Rolls but these are the
exception rather than the rule.

County Record Offices

Returns show that many offices have no master index covering all documents of the
war period. Most acknowledged that they held records within their Civil Parish and
Urban District Council collections but as these were not included in the WWI index
they could not provide a detailed list. A few mentioned classes of record not included
in the questionnaire, Absent Voters' Lists being typical. In all probability these would
be held by many CROs. Where held, military records appear to be well indexed.

  Bedfordshire, Suffolk and Sussex CROs are among those who hold a
comprehensive index and a glance through the entries for those offices will give an
idea of the type of records covered.

Libraries

Only a few were contacted and the replies revealed many printed histories and Rolls
of Honour, including some of the latter not in the British Library Catalogue.

Books

It is hoped that at least one book on the history of each Regiment or Corps for the
war period has been included. Reference should always be made to *A Bibliography of
Regimental Histories of the British Army* by A.S. White (published in 1988 by The
London Stamp Exchange for The Society for Army Historical Research), particularly

when dealing with Corps (Bibl.Ref. 8) as books on Corps units have not as a rule been included. Very few books of soldiers' reminiscences have been mentioned. The card index in the IWM is arranged by unit and will locate some of the rarer books.

Rolls of Honour

The many Rolls of Honour and/or Service held by the IWM have not been included. Any lists still held in private hands that have been found have been offered to the IWM.

The IWM has two card indexes and both must be checked. Rolls of Honour are included in Section 25 (New Library) and 33.4 (41) (Old Library).

All Rolls of Honour are listed in the BL Subject Catalogue under European War – Rolls of Honour. These have been included even if they only contain lists of those killed.

Almost every parish church or parish has a memorial plaque showing the names of those killed

Additional Rolls of Honour

As well as those Lists of Rolls of Service which follow on pages 22 to 25, there are a number of Rolls of Honour/Service for Schools and University Colleges. To save space, the titles have been abbreviated but full details may be found in the BL Printed Books Catalogue or check with the local library.

Schools. Oundle, Dragon (Oxford), Brighton College, Sedbergh, Oxford High School, Rugby, St. Bees (Edinburgh), Royal (Shrewsbury), Wycliffe College (Stonehouse, Glos.), Cheltenham, St. George (Downside), Eton, Lewisham Grammar, Protestant Dissenters Grammar (Mill Hill), Eastbourne College, Northampton, St. Cuthbert's (Worksop), Elizabeth College (Guernsey), Harrow, Malabar House (Oxford), King Edward's (Birmingham), Bournemouth, Denstone College, Haileybury (Hertford), Stonyhurst, Newton Abbott, Plymouth College, Portsmouth Grammar, Repton, Shrewsbury, St. Katharines (Southbourne), Trent, Winchester.

University colleges. Gonville and Caius, Manchester, Oxford, Wadham (Oxford), Ireland (Dublin), Corpus Christi (Oxford), Pembroke (Cambridge), Durham, Wales, Christ College (Brecon).

Lists of Rolls of Service covering the Whole Country

The British (Museum) Library. (Catalogued under European War – Roll of Honour).
The Imperial War Museum Collection.
The National Army Museum Collection.
The Society of Genealogists' Collection.
Ireland's Memorial Records 1914–18, 8 Volumes
London County Westminster and Paris Bank Ltd. Record of Service of Solicitors and Articled Clerks with HM Forces 1914–19.

North British and Mercantile Insurance Co. Ltd; active service list 1914–19.
Prudential Staff and the Great War.
War Book of Gray's Inn.
British Jewry Roll of Honour, Rev. M. Adler, Caxton, 1922.
Most railway companies printed lists of men who served, e.g. GWR, LNWR, Brighton and S. Coast.
Wisden Cricketers' Almanac, 1916, containing 80 obituaries of cricketers who died in the war.
The War Memorial Collection of the Lancashire FH&HS (formerly the Rossendale Society for Genealogy and Heraldry) includes items from all over the UK.
Western Union Roll of Honour, Unitarian and Free Christian Churches. Covers SW England area. See Nottingham University Library entry for details.
Muster Roll of the Manse, D. Cameron (Glasgow Local Collection).
Oxford University Roll of Service, E.S.Craig, 2 Volumes (1914–16 and 1914–15).
National Union of Teachers' War Record 1914–19, 207 pages, 1920 (BL.08364.cc.7).
Bulletin in Honour of the Staff of the British American Tobacco Co. who have joined HM Forces, BAT Co., 1915 (BL.PP.1423.fpc).
The Roll of Honour, Marquis de Ruvigny, The Standard Art Book Co. Ltd.. London. In five volumes with many portraits. Gives a potted biography of each man but gives only some 25,000 names out of the 500,000. Reprinted as 2 Volumes in 1987 by the London Stamp Exchange. (Limited Edition of 100 copies.)
Coutts and Co. Bankers. Record of Service of Members of the Staff in the Great War 1914–18, 1922 (BL.9085.cc.10).
Portraits of Lloyds' Men whose Names Appear on Lloyds' War Memorial, Lloyds, 1922 (BL.9081.d.2).
War Record of the Great Western Railways, E.A. Pratt, Selwyn & Blount, 1922, (BL 8235.r.10).
London and North Western Railway Company's Roll of Honour 1914–19, 1921 (BL.1878.cc.6).
Record of War Service of Rhodes Scholars from the Dominions Beyond the Seas and the United States of America, 1920 (BL.09080.aa.47).
The Rugby Football Internationals' Roll of Honour, E.H.D. Sewell, T.C. Jack, 1919 (BL 10803.h.17).
For Remembrance. Soldier Poets who have fallen in the War, A.St.J. Adcock, Hodder & Stoughton, 1920 (BL.01083.f.13).
Roll of Honour and List of North Eastern Railway Men Serving in the Navy and Army, N.E.R. Co., York, 1915 (BL.8235.f.64).
Institution of Civil Engineers. Memorial Volume containing a Record of the Members and Students who died for their Country 1914–19, 1924 (BL.9034.h.1).
Masonic Roll of Honour. Names of Brethren who fell in the Service of their King and Country during the Great War 1914–18, Freemasons' Hall, 1921, (BL.04782.f.24).

23

The House of Commons Book of Remembrance, E.W.M. Blundell, Matthews & Marrot, 1931 (BL.09080.d.22).

Loretto School Roll of Honour 1914–20, 1922, (BL.08368.cc.2).

The Unveiling of the Stock Exchange War Memorial, Stock Exchange, 1923 (BL.9101.dd.20).

Roll of the Sons and Daughters of the Anglican Church Clergy throughout the World, and of Naval and Military Chaplains of the same, who gave their lives in the Great War, by R. Ussher, English Crafts and Monumental Society, 1925 (BL.9085.cc.6).

British Public Schools War Memorials, C.F. Kernot, Roberts & Newton, 1927 (BL.8366.i.22).

The Roll of Honour of the Institution of Electrical Engineers (1914–19), W.A.J. O'Meara, 1924 (BL.1854.h.4).

With the Colours. A List of Chartered and Incorporated Accountants and their Clerks who are serving with the British Forces 1914–16, Gee & Co., 1916 (BL.8824.i.29).

Roll of Honour of British Libraries, Library Association Record Pamphlet No.1 (BL.R.Ac.9115/19).

Public Schools and the Great War 1914–19, A.H.H. Maclean, (BL.09084.cc.20).

National Roll of Honour, 14 Volumes. Very incomplete. IWM, SOG or local library.

The Officers' Training Corps Roll, Tom Donovan. A roll of members and ex-members of the OTC gazetted to commissions in the Army August 1914–March 1915. Lists 16,000 names but still only 80% complete.

The Soldiers of Caterham 1914–18, Peter Saater, 1984. Contains 231 names.

Roll of Honour. An Illustrated Record of the Men of Deal, Walmer, Sandwich and District, T.F. Pain of the Mercury Newspaper, five Volumes. Lists 100 men with photo and details of family.

Overseas Rolls of Service

Melbourne Grammar School Australia War Service, SOG.

British Columbia Canada Record of University Service 1914–18, SOG.

The Victoria Oarsman with a Rowing Register, John Lang, Melbourne, Australia, 1919. Lists 1380 members of Victorian Rowing Club.

Activities of the British Community in Argentina during the Great War 1914–18, British Society, 1920.

Huguenot Society Proceedings, Vol. XII, 288, 483; Vol. XV, 173. Guildhall Library.

War Memorials, F. Weitenkampf. A list of references in the New York Public Library (USA), New York, 1919 (BL.11909.p.1/93).

Roll of Honour of Ceylonese who served in the Great War, A.S. Eaton, 1930 (BL.CS.43).

Melbourne University Record of Active Service of Teachers, Graduates, Undergraduates, Officers and Servants in the European War, Melbourne, 1926 (BL.8385.i.22).

Australian Jewry, Book of Honour. The Great War 1914–18 H. Boas, Perth, 1923, (BL.983.c.51).

The Education Department's Record of War Service 1914–19, Victoria, Australia; Melbourne, 1921 (BL.9083.ff.20).

Roll of Honour, W. Jaggard, 1920 (BL Old Copyright office). A typescript list of about 50,000 officers and ORs who came overseas to join HM Forces in the Great War and who were repatriated through Winchester Repatriation Camp in 1919–20.

5

CORPS TROOPS

ROYAL ARTILLERY

(Royal Horse Artillery, Royal Field Artillery, Royal Garrison Artillery)

Until recently there has been no history of the Royal Artillery in the Great War. Now, however, the first volume has appeared — *History of the Royal Regiment of Artillery, Western Front 1914–18* by General Sir Martin Farndale, Royal Artillery Institute.

In addition the following may be useful:
The Royal Artillery War Commemoration Book, published on behalf of the RA War Commemoration Fund by G. Bell & Sons Ltd, 1920.

The History of Coast Artillery in the British Army, Colonel K.W. Maurice-Jones, Royal Artillery Institute, 1959.

The Long March. The story of The Devil's Own. B/210 (Burnley) Battery, Royal Field Artillery, Jack Horsfall, 23 Jenner Close, Hucclescote, Glos. GL3 2DZ. (300pp.) Besides giving details of the unit, it is an excellent example of what can be found out about an ancestor's war service.

There are many other books, often with full lists of personnel who served, dealing with individual batteries (Bibl.Ref. 8).

As the Royal Flying Corps co-operated to a great extent with the artillery in spotting targets, etc. the Air War History includes many mentions of the location of gun batteries. Those having Artillery ancestors should not neglect this source.

The War in the Air, Sir W. Raleigh and H.A. Jones, Oxford University Press, Volumes 1–5, Hamish Hamilton.

Museum
Old Royal Military Academy, Red Lion Lane, Woolwich, London SE18 4DN.
There are no lists of men other than those in books.

CRO
Many Artillery units were manned by Territorial Force men and in fact were named as TF units. The records of these TF units sometimes end up in the local CRO. A list of the TF Artillery units, with counties, is given in AC1 2198 Nov 1916 Appendix 183; PRO Kew WO293/5.

CORPS OF ROYAL ENGINEERS

This consisted of some 400 units.

Books

History of the Corps of Royal Engineers, The Royal Engineers Institution, Chatham, various authors and dates.

Volume 3, Colonel Sir Charles M. Watson, 1915.

Volume 4, Brigadier-General W. Baker-Brown, 1952.

Volume 5, The Home Front, France, Flanders and Italy in the First World War, 1952.

Volume 6, Gallipoli, Macedonia, Egypt and Palestine 1914–18, 1952.

Volume 7, Campaigns in Mesopotamia and E. Africa and the inter-war period 1919–38, 1952.

The Work of the RE in the European War 1914–18, The Royal Engineers Institution, Chatham, 1921–27, (10 vols). Technical details only; no details of work of units or men.

Autobiography by Francis Victor Merchant. Deals with signals.

The Signal Service in the European War of 1914–18, R.E. Prestly, Royal Engineers Institution and Signals Association, Chatham, 1921.

Pigeons in the Great War, A.H. Osman, Racing Pigeon, London, 1929.

23rd Field Coy in the Great War 1914–18, Royal Engineers Institution.

History of the 95th Field Coy, Adlard & Sons and West Newman, 1919.

A Record of the 203rd Field Coy 1915–19, Heffer & Son, 1921.

Narrative of 502 (Wessex) Field Coy 1915–19, published by Rees, 1920.

The Poisonous Cloud. Chemical Warfare in the First World War, L.F. Haber, Clarendon Press.

Gas. History of the Special Brigade RE, H. Foulkes, Blackwood, 1934. Covers British use of gas.

Artillery. Survey in the First World War, Sir Lawrence Bragg, Major-General A.H. Dowson and Lieutenant-Colonel H.H. Hemming, 1971.

Tunnellers. The Story of the Tunnelling Companies, RE during the World War, Captain Grant Grieve and Bernard Newman, 1936.

War Underground. Tunnellers of the Great War, Alexander Barrie, 1932. Reprinted by *Narrow Gauge at War,* K. Taylorson, 1987. The work of the narrow gauge railways in the war.

The Railway Gazette Special War Transportation Number, 21st Sep 1920.

Bibliography of Regimental Histories, S.A. White. Lists some 20 other books dealing with individual units. Besides the main entry, check the Territorial Force units listed by counties from page 178.

Museums

The Royal Engineers Museum. Brompton Barracks. Chatham, Kent ME4 4UG. Has a WWI Gallery.

The Royal Logistic Corps Museum, RLC Training Centre, Princess Royal Barracks, Blackdown, Deepcut, Camberley Surrey GU16 6RW.
RE Courier and Postal Services.
The Royal Corps of Signals Museum, Blandford Camp, Dorset.
Has the diaries of Lieutenant D. Findlay, Colonel J.W. Cohan (3 volumes), Lieutenant J.R. Pinsent and F.B. (Cable) Section. (Army Signals were the responsibility of the Royal Engineers until the formation of the Royal Corps of Signals after the 1914–18 War.) Also Coy. Order Book, West Lancs, Div. Sig. Coy RE (1915–) and Nominal Roll, 23rd Div. Sig. Coy RE. Narrative J.H.S. Christian.
Notes on Sapper S. Bennett 22 Coy RE.
The RE Corps Library, Institution of Royal Engineers, Chatham, Kent.
Has most of the books plus a number of manuscripts and diaries dealing with the 400 units.
There are no lists of men as such but some books do have, as an appendix, a list of all who served.

CRO
Cornwall hold a Nominal Roll of the 573 A.T. Coy. RE Nov 1914 to Mar 1919. (Ref. DC/St. Austell – Fowey 215)

LABOUR CORPS

Books
No known books other than
With a Labour Company in France, Captain T.C. Thomas, Hudson & Son, 1919. The War Diary of the 58th Labour Coy.
China on the Western Front. Britain's Chinese Work-Force in the First World War, M. Summerskill, London, 1983.

Museum
There is no museum.
It is worth noting that many men were transferred to the Labour Corps after convalescing from wounds if they were considered not fit enough for further front line service.

THE TERRITORIAL FORCE

The list of Regiments at the head of each County section does not as a rule include the various TF Artillery, Engineer, Army Service and Medical Corps units under the control of the County Territorial Force Association. A more complete list, with a brief history of each unit, is to be found in *His Majesty's Territorial Army* by Walter Richards, Virtue & Co., c1910.
A more modern book gives similar detail. *The Territorial Force 1914* by Ray Westlake (1988) shows all units of the TF at the start of the war. There is also a history of the TF, *The Territorial Army 1907–40* by Peter Denis, Royal Historical Society, The Boydell Press, 1987.

Forward Everywhere. Her Majesty's Territorials by Stanley Simm Baldwin, Brasseys, 1994 has three chapters on WWI including an account of the FANY and other Women's Services.

THE NATIONAL GUARD

Books

The National Guard in the Great War 1914–18, A.E. Manning Foster, Cope & Fenwick, 1920.

Museum

There is no known museum.

ARMY PHYSICAL TRAINING CORPS

Books

History of the Army Physical Training Corps, Lieutenant-Colonel E.A.L. Oldfield, Gale & Polden, 1955.

Museum

Queen's Avenue, Aldershot, Hampshire GU11 2LB.

ROYAL MILITARY POLICE

Books

History of the Office of the Provost Marshal and the Corps of Military Police, A.V. Lovell-Knight.

The History of the Corps of Royal Military Police, Major F.S.Crozier.

The Story of the Royal Military Police, A.V. Lovell-Knight, Seeley Service, 1977.

Bloody Provost, R.A.V. Tyler, Phillimore 1977.

FSP, A. Gwynne-Brown, Chatto & Windus 1942.

  None of these give details of men but are general works.

Museum

Roussillon Barracks, Chichester, Sussex PO19 4BN.

  No lists of men held.

ROYAL ARMY CHAPLAINS DEPARTMENT

Books

Ministering to the Forces, Rev. Ronald W. Thomson, Baptist Union of Great Britain and Ireland and the Congregational Union of England and Wales, 1964.

The Church of England and the First World War, Alan Wilkinson, SPCK, 1978.

God on our Side, Michael Moynihan (Ed.), A Leo Cooper Book, 1983.

  None of these have lists of names.

Museum

Bagshot Park, Bagshot, Surrey GU19 5PL.

THE MACHINE GUN CORPS

Books

Machine Guns. A History of the Machine Gun Corps, G.S. Hutchinson, Macmillan, 1938.

The Machine Gunner 1914–18, C.E. Crutchley (Ed.), Bailey Brothers and Swinfen, 1973. A compilation of experiences of members of the Corps.

Seven Year Saga. The Story of the MGC 1915–22, Norman Edwards and David Woodward. Article in *Vickers Magazine.*

A.S. White lists histories of the 1st Machine Gun Squadron, 20th Machine Gun Squadron, 33rd Bn. MGC, 19th, 98th, 100th, 248th M.G. Coys, 110th MG Coy 21st Div.

Museum

There is no museum.

ROYAL ARMY ORDNANCE CORPS

Books

History of the Army Ordnance Services, Vols. 1–3, Major-General A. Forbes, The Medici Society Ltd, 1929. Volume 3 deals with the Great War.

Museum

The Royal Logistic Corps Museum, RLC Training Centre, Princess Royal Barracks, Blackdown, Deepcut, Camberley Surrey GU16 6RW.

The museum has a Roll of Regular NCOs 1904–22; includes Stores Branch, Artificers and Armourers Sections. There is also an index of about 3000 names taken from the *AOC/RAOC Gazette.*

Other records

PRO Kew. Some names in WO 111/13.

CORPS OF ARMY SCHOOL MASTERS

Books

The Story of Army Education 1643–1963, A.C.T. White.

Adult Education. The Record of the British Army, Hawkin and Brimble, Macmillan.

Education and the Army. Reorganised Army Education 1918–20, Lord Gorell, Oxford University Press, 1921.

Tommy Atkins' Children, John Williams, HMSO, 1971.

Museum

Royal Army Educational Corps Museum, Wilton Park, Beaconsfield, Bucks HP9 2RP.

Has a few press cuttings and some memoirs. Some lists of Senior Ranks. Very few members of the Corps served on active operations.

ROYAL ARMY PAY CORPS

Books

The Royal Army Pay Corps, Colonel L.H. Mackenzie, The Chester Press, 1951.

Trust and be Trusted, Brigadier L.G. Hinchliffe, Corps HQ, 1983.

Museum

Corps H.Q., Worthy Down, Winchester, Hampshire SO21 2RG.

Very few records. May have a few details of pre-war Regulars and some 1914–18 men.

ARMY SERVICE CORPS

Books

Royal Army Service Corps. A History of Transport and Supply in the British Army, Colonel R.H. Beadon, Vol. 2, Cambridge University Press, 1930. Covers the Great War.

Transportation on the Western Front 1914–18, Colonel A.M. Henniker. One volume plus map case.

Neither of these two books mention men but do provide details of type of unit. As ASC units and detached groups of men served with other Corps, the histories of these should also be studied, e.g. the ASC provided transport for the Artillery and for the RAMC. There are a number of books on individual units; see A.S. White (details on p. 21), for example.

Memorials of the 71st and 83rd Companies RASC, MT, 1914–18, Stanley J. Levy, 1931.

Grove Park in the Great War, John King, Grove Park Community Group, 1983. Includes photos and description of A.S.C M.T. Training Depot.

The Story of the Romsey Remount Depot, Colonel Sir Herbert Jessel, Abbey Press, 1920. This is the day-to-day diary of the work of the Army's main depot for the provision of horses.

Museum

The Royal Logistic Corps Museum, RLC Training Centre, Princess Royal Barracks, Blackdown, Deepcut, Camberley, Surrey GU16 6RW.

Has no lists of men except a few manuscript ledgers of pre-1914 Regulars without details of unit. There are manuscript or typed potted histories of approx. 1000 transport units but none has lists other than a few which give those killed and recipients of awards. There is a large photographic collection and a few books of orders.

THE TANK CORPS

Books

The Tanks, B.H. Liddell Hart, Vols. 1 and 2, Cassell 1959.

The Tank Corps Book of Honour, Major R.F.G. Maurice, Spottiswoode, Ballantyne & Co. Ltd., 1919.

Seconds Out, K. Chadwick.
Short History of the 2nd Battalion in the Great War, author unknown.
History of the 13th Battalion, Major Maurice, Andrew Menrose Ltd.
History of the 14th Battalion, author unknown.
Tank and AFV Uniforms since 1916, Martin Windrow. Gives battalion emblems.
Tank Warfare. The Story of the Tanks in the Great War, Francis Mitchell, 1933.
A.S. White lists ten further books.

Museum
Royal Armoured Corps & Royal Tank Regiment Museum, Bovington, Dorset BH20 5JG.
Has an extensive library and photographic library but no records of men.

ROYAL ARMY VETERINARY CORPS

Books
History of the Royal Army Veterinary Corps 1796–1919, Major-General Sir Frederick Smith, Bailliere, Tindall & Cox, 1927.
Veterinary Services. History of the Great War. Medical, Major-General Sir L.J.Blenkinsop and Lieutenant Colonel J.W.Ramey, (Eds.), HMSO. Part of the Official History series.
Try *The Veterinary History Society* and *The Veterinary Journal* for the period of the War.

Museum
Gallwey Road, Aldershot, Hampshire GU11 2DQ.
No lists of men held.

THE ROYAL ARMY MEDICAL CORPS

Books
Medical History of the Great War. General History, Major-General Sir W.G. Macpherson, HMSO, Vols. 1–4. No lists, but enables most units to be traced. Volume 3 has a complete list of units.
3rd East Anglian Field Ambulance. A record, 1914–19, author unknown, ca. 1920. Lists all men serving. (Essex CRO)
The Friends Ambulance Unit 1914–19, Meaburn Tatham and James E. Miles, Swarthmore Press, 1919.
A.S. White lists a number of books on individual units both Regular and TF.

Museum
Keogh Barracks, Ash Vale, Nr. Aldershot, Hampshire GU12 5RQ.
The Museum has no lists and a large part of the collection is held in the MoD Library, Medical Section, which is not open to the public.

Other Records
Casualties and Medical Statistics, Major T.J. Mitchell and Miss G.M. Smith, HMSO, 1931. Describes the medical records now in PRO, Kew MH 106/...

THE ROYAL MARINES

Books
Britain's Sea Soldiers. A Record of the Royal Marines during the War 1914–19, General Sir H.E. Blumberg, Devonport, 1927.

Museum
Royal Marines' Barracks, Eastney, Portsmouth, Hampshire PO4 9PX.
   Not contacted.

6

THE WOMEN'S SERVICES

There are several general books on the Women's' Services including *Women in Khaki* by Roy Terry.

QUEEN ALEXANDRA'S IMPERIAL MILITARY NURSING SERVICE

Books
Overseas Records of the TF Nursing Service 1914–20, author unknown (Museum).
One Hundred Years of Army Nursing. The Story of the British Army Nursing Service from the Time of Florence Nightingale to the Present Day, Ian Hay, Cassel & Co. Ltd., 1952.
Reminiscent Sketches 1914–19, by members of Her Majesty Queen Alexandra's Imperial Military Nursing Service, John Bale & Sons & Danielson Ltd., 1922.

Museum
RHQ, Royal Pavilion, Farnborough Road, Aldershot, Hampshire GU11 1PZ.
    The museum has no records but the War Diaries of most Casualty Clearing Stations and Hospitals list the arrival and departure of nurses.

Other records
Journal of Orders and Medals Society, Vol. 8, No. 2, June 1969 reports that the service grew from 300 + 800 reserves in 1914 to 10,000. 36 killed; 195 died from all causes.

PRO records
Pension records 1909–28, PMG34/1–5 and PMG42/1–12. Appointments 1903–26 WO25/3956. Medical records MH106/2207–2211.
    See also PRO Leaflet No. 120 *Military Nurses and Nursing Services: Record Sources in the Public Record office.*

THE FIRST AID NURSING YEOMANRY

Founded 1907. Ran self-contained Motor Ambulance Units in France 1914–18.

Books
Fanny Went to War, Pat Beauchamp, John Murray, 1919.
Fany. The Story of the Women's' Transport Service 1907–84 Hugh Popham, Leo Cooper, 1986.
F.A.N.Y. Invicta, Irene Ward.

Museum
Apply in writing to Corps Commander, E Block, Duke of York's HQ, King's Road, Chelsea, London SW 4SJ.

THE WOMEN'S ARMY AUXILIARY CORPS (formed 1917)
QUEEN MARY'S ARMY AUXILIARY CORPS (May 1918)

Books
Short History of Queen Mary's Army Auxiliary Corps, Colonel J.M. Cowper.
Service with the Army, Dame H. Gwynne-Vaughan, Hutchinson, 1941.

Museum
The former museum at the WRAC Centre, Queen Elizabeth Park, Guildford has now been transferred to the National Army Museum, Royal Hospital Road, Chelsea, London SW1P 2DX.

The museum had few documents of interest but recommended the following call Nos.: MC 2331, MC 108, MC 2530, MC 2188, MC 625, MC 75, MC 56, MC 2200, SCD 20, SCD 58, SCD 912, SCD 764, SCD 25, SCD 6, SC 768, SC303. Next-of-kin might enquire if the ancestor appears on any roll.

Other records
PRO Kew. Part nominal roll for QMAAC WO162/16.

THE WOMEN'S LEGIONS (1915–19)

No information.

VOLUNTARY AID DETACHMENTS (VADs)

Records are held by the International Red Cross Society, c/o The Archivist, British Red Cross Training Centre, Barnett Hill, Wonersh, Guildford, Surrey GU5 3PJ.

Books
Red Cross and the Order of St. John of Jerusalem, 1921, 823pp. Reports by the Joint War Finance Committee of the BRCS and OSJJ in England on Voluntary Aid rendered to the Sick and Wounded at Home and Abroad and to POW's 1914–19.
Sisters' Quarters. Salonika, Marguerite Fedden, Grant Richards, 1921. The story of a VAD in the Eastern Mediterranean.
A VAD in France, Olive Dent, Grant Richards, 1917.
For Dauntless France. An Account of Britain's Aid to the French Wounded and Victims of War, Laurence Binyon, Hodder & Stoughton, 1918.

7

OTHER UNITS

CANADIAN ARMY

)etails of Canadian Army Personnel can be obtained from Personnel Records
'entre, National Archives of Canada, 395 Wellington Street, Ottawa, Ontario,
'anada K1A 0N3. Reply may take several months. See *Family History News and
)igest,* April 1986, p.134.

CANTEENS AND ENTERTAINERS

Books
Vest and East with the EFC, Captain E. Vredenbury, Raphael Tuck & Sons. The
:ory of the Expedition Forces Canteens. ContaINS photographs of staff, etc.

8

REGIMENTS WITH NO OBVIOUS PLACE OF ORIGIN

THE HONOURABLE ARTILLERY COMPANY

Acted as an Officer Training Unit during the War, mainly for men who became officers in the various branches of the Artillery.

Books

The HAC in the Great War, Major G. Goold Walker, 1929.

HAC Journal, 1922 issues give details of WWI men.

London Gunners. The Story of the HAC Siege Battery in Action, W.R. Kingham Methuen, 1919.

Museum

Armoury House, City Road, London EC1Y 2BQ.

Has an Honorary Archivist who is also a genealogist. The museum has a complete list of men which covers the time up to the point they were posted to other Regiment and Corps. There are many records at present in process of being indexed. There is small charge for a search to be made in the records. A stamped, addressed envelope or 3 International Reply Coupons must accompany all enquiries.

Printed lists of pre-war members of the Company are held in the Guildhal Library.

CRO

The Surrey CRO, Kingston has a Recruitment Book (Ref. 2496/26) for the period Mar—5 Sep 1917 but this probably refers to conscripted men who had to 'register' at the Company's depot and not to potential officer trainees (not checked).

THE RIFLE BRIGADE

Books

History of the Rifle Brigade in the War 1914—19, Vols. 1 and 2, with Foreword by the Duke of Connaught, The Rifle Brigade Club Ltd., 1927.

For the Duration. The Story of the 13th Battalion The Rifle Brigade, D.H. Rowland Simpkin, Marshall Ltd., 1932.

The Rifle Brigade Chronicle for 1914–20, Vols. 1–7, Colonel Willoughby Verner (Ed.). Contains many Nominal Rolls.

Museum
The Royal Green Jackets Museum, Pensinular Barracks, Romsey Road, Winchester, Hampshire SO23 8TS.
No lists of men held.

THE KING'S ROYAL RIFLE CORPS

Books
The Annals of the King's Royal Rifle Corps, Vol. 5, *The Great War,* Major-General Sir Steuart Hare, John Murray, 1932.
Short History of the 20th Battalion King's Royal Rifle Corps (BEL Pioneers) 1915–19, Captain A.S. Turberville, Goddard, Walker & Brown Ltd, 1923.

Museum
The Royal Green Jackets Museum, Peninsular Barracks, Romsey Road, Winchester, Hampshire SO23 8TS.
No lists of men held.

THE GUARDS

Regiments
 The Grenadier Guards   The Scots Guards
 The Coldstream Guards   The Irish Guards
 The Welsh Guards (formed in 1915)
 The 4th (Foot Guards) Battalion, The Guards Machine Gun Regiment

Books
The Grenadier Guards in the Great War of 1914–18, Vols. 1–3, Lieutenant-Colonel Sir Frederick Ponsonby, Macmillan, 1920.
The Coldstream Guards 1914–18, Vols. 1 and 2 with map case, Lieutenant-Colonel Sir John Ross of Bladensburg, Oxford University Press, 1928.
The Scots Guards in the Great War 1914–18, F. Loraine Petre, John Murray, 1925.
The Irish Guards in the Great War, Rudyard Kipling (Ed.), Macmillan, 1923.
History of the Welsh Guards, C.H. Dudley Ward, John Murray, 1920.
The Welch Regiment of Foot Guards 1915–18, C.H. Dudley Ward.

Museums
Guards Museum, Wellington Barracks, Birdcage Walk, London SW1E 6HQ.
 Combined Record Office (same address) has records of all guardsmen. They may be able to help next-of-kin. A charge is made for research.
Coldstream Museum, 13 Market Square, Coldstream, Berwickshire, Scotland.

9

CAVALRY REGIMENTS

THE HOUSEHOLD CAVALRY

Regiments

1st Life Guards	2nd Life Guards
Royal Horse Guards	Household Cavalry Composite Regiment
Guards Divisional Cavalry Squadron	
1st, 2nd, 3rd Bns. Guards Machine Gun Regiment	

Books

The History of the Household Cavalry, Vol. 3, Sir George Artheur, Wm. Heineman Ltd., 1926.

Museum

Household Cavalry Records Office, Household Cavalry Museum, Combermere Barracks, Windsor, Berks SL4 3DN.

Has very good records of the 1914—18 men.

1ST (KING'S DRAGOON GUARDS

Books

Short History of the Kings Dragoon Guards 1685—1929, Gale & Polden. Gives a list of wounded. A short book for use by recruits.

Museum

Cardiff Castle, Cardiff CF1 2RB.

No lists of men held.

2ND DRAGOON GUARDS (QUEEN'S BAYS)

Books

History of the Queens's Bays, 2nd Dragoon Guards 1685—1929, Fred Whyte and A Hilliard Atteridge (Eds.), Jonathan Cape, 1930. No list of men.

Museum

Cardiff Castle, Cardiff CF1 2RB.

No lists of men held.

3RD (PRINCE OF WALES'S) DRAGOON GUARDS

Books

History of the 3rd (Prince of Wales) Dragoon Guards 1914–18, Captain H.P. Holt, Billing & Sons, 1937.

Museum

Home HQ, Royal Dragoon Guards, 3 Tower Street, York YO1 1SB.
No lists of men held.

4TH (ROYAL IRISH) DRAGOON GUARDS

Books

Records of the 4th Royal Irish Dragoon Guards in the Great War 1914–18, Rev. Harold Gibb, Canterbury, 1925.

Museum

Home HQ, Royal Dragoon Guards, 3 Tower Street, York YO1 1SB.
Has 3 volumes of Regimental Rolls 1914–19 plus some records of illegal absences by soldiers 1915–39. List of wounded.

5TH (PRINCESS CHARLOTTE OF WALES'S) DRAGOON GUARDS

Books

Story of a Regiment of Horse. Being the Regimental History from 1685–1922 of the 5th (Princess Charlotte of Wales) Dragoon Guards, Major R.L. Pomeroy, W. Blackwood & Son, 1924.

Museum

Home HQ, Royal Dragoon Guards, 3 Tower Street, York YO1 1SB.

6TH DRAGOON GUARDS (CARABINIERS)

Books

No known books.

Museum

The Castle, Edinburgh EH1 2YT.
No lists of men held.

7TH (PRINCESS ROYAL'S) DRAGOON GUARDS

Books

Records of the 7th Dragoon Guards during the Great War, Captain F.J. Scott, F. Bennett & Co., 1923.

Museum

Home HQ, Royal Dragoon Guards, 3 Tower Street, York YO1 1SB.

1ST (ROYAL) DRAGOONS

Books
History of the Royal Dragoons 1661–1934, C.T. Atkinson, Glasgow, printed for the Regiment 1934.

Museum
Combermere Barracks, Windsor, Berkshire SL4 3DN.
No lists of men held.

2ND DRAGOONS (ROYAL SCOTS GREYS)

Books
History of the Royal Scots Greys (2nd Dragoons) August 1914–March 1919, Major R Pomeroy and Colonel W.F. Collins, 1932.

Museum
The Castle, Edinburgh EH1 2YT.
Has a few records including Regimental Orders but no lists of men.

3RD (KING'S OWN) HUSSARS

Books
The 3rd (King's Own) Hussars in the Great War, Lieutenant-Colonel W.T. Willcox, John Murray, 1925. Contains Nominal Roll.

Museum
The Lord Leycester Hospital, High Street, Warwick CV34 4EW.

4TH (QUEEN'S OWN) HUSSARS

Books
The 4th (Queen's Own) Hussars in the Great War, Captain H.K.D. Evans, Gale & Polden, 1920.

Museum
Sussex Combined Services Museum, Redoubt Fortress, Royal Parade, Eastbourne, Sussex BN22 7AQ.
No lists of men held.

5TH (ROYAL IRISH) LANCERS

Books
No known books

Museum
Belvoir Castle, nr. Grantham, Lincolnshire NG33 7TJ.
List of casualties, awards, copies of the Regimental periodical 1914–19.

6TH (INNISKILLING) DRAGOONS

Books
No known books.

Museum
The Castle, Edinburgh EH1 2YT.
A few records but mostly confined to Regimental orders.

7TH (QUEEN'S OWN) HUSSARS

Books
The Years Between. The Story of the 7th (Queen's Own) Hussars 1911–37, Major-General Roger Evans, Gale & Polden, 1965.

Museum
The Lord Leycester Hospital, High Street, Warwick CV34 4EW.

8TH (KING'S ROYAL IRISH) HUSSARS

Books
History of the 8th King's Royal Irish Hussars 1693–1927, Vol. 2, Rev.R.H. Murray, W. Heffer, 1928.

Museum
Sussex Combined Services Museum, Redoubt Fortress, Royal Parade, Eastbourne, Sussex BN22 7AQ.
No lists of men held.

9TH (QUEEN'S ROYAL) LANCERS

Books
The Ninth Queen's Royal Lancers 1715–1936, Major E.W. Shepherd, Gale & Polden Ltd., Aldershot, 1939.
A Short History of the 9th Queen's Royal Lancers 1715–1949, Major W. Hanwell, Gale & Polden Ltd., Aldershot, 1949.

Museum
Derby City Museum and Art Gallery, The Strand, Derby DE1 1BS.
All records now with the NAM, Chelsea. Details not known.

10TH (PRINCE OF WALES'S OWN ROYAL) HUSSARS

Books
The 10th Hussars (Prince of Wales's Own) and the Essex Yeomanry During the European War 1914–18, Lieutenant-Colonel F.H.D.C. Whitmore, Benham & Co. Ltd., 1920.

Museum
Peninsular Barracks, Winchester, Hampshire SO23 8TS.
No lists of men held.

11TH (PRINCE ALBERT'S OWN) HUSSARS

Books
History of the 11th Hussars (Prince Albert's Own) 1908–34, Captain L.R. Lumley
Royal United Services Institution, 1936.

Museum
Peninsular Barracks, Winchester, Hampshire SO23 8TS.
No lists of men held.

12TH (PRINCE OF WALES'S ROYAL) LANCERS

Books
The Story of the XII Royal Lancers from 1715 to 1918, Lt.Col. G.W. Hobson, Xpress
Printers Ltd., Northampton, 1945.
The 12th Royal Lancers in France August 17th 1914 – November 11th 1918, Major
H.V.S. Charrington, Gale & Polden Ltd., Aldershot, 1921.
The History of the 12th Royal Lancers, Captain P.T. Stewart, Oxford University
Press, 1950.

Museum
Derby City Museum, The Strand, Derby E1 1BS.
All records now with the NAM, Chelsea. Details not known.

13TH HUSSARS

Books
The 13th Hussars in the Great War, by Rt. Hon. Sir H.M. Durand, Wm. Blackwood
1921.

Museum
Cannon Hall Museum & Art Gallery, Cawthorne, Barnsley, S. Yorkshire S75 4AT.

14TH (KING'S) HUSSARS

Books
Historical Record of the 14th (King's) Hussars from 1900–22, Vol. 2, Brigadier J.
Gilbert Browne and Lieutenant-Colonel E.J. Bridges, Royal United Services Inst.,
1932.
Emperor's Chambermaids. The Story of the 14th/20th King's Hussars, Lieutenant-
Colonel L.B. Oates, DSO.

Museum
Lancashire County & Regimental Museum, Stanley St., Preston, Lancs. PR1 4YP.
No lists of men held.

15TH (THE KING'S) HUSSARS

Books
History of the 15th The King's Hussars 1914–22, Lord Carnock, The Crypt House
Press, 1932.
Museum
A Soldier's Life, Newcastle Discovery, Blandford House, Blandford Square,
Newcastle-upon-Tyne NE1 4JA. (Mr Ralph Thompson)
Registration Forms (Call No. D/8); Regimental orders of 14th Reserve Cavalry
Regiment (D.516); 15th Hussars OCA Reports (C/26).

16TH (THE QUEEN'S) LANCERS

Books
History of the Sixteenth, The Queen's Light Dragoons (Lancers) 1912–1925, Col.
Henry Graham, Devizes, privately printed, 1926.
Museum
Belvoir Castle, nr. Grantham, Lincolnshire NG33 7TJ.
No lists of men held.

17TH (DUKE OF CABBRIDGE'S OWN) LANCERS

Books
A History of the 17th Lancers (Duke of Cambridge's Own), Vol.2 1895–1924, Major
Gilbert Nicholls, Macmillan & Co. Ltd., London, 1931.
Museum
Belvoir Castle, nr. Grantham, Lincolnshire NG33 7TJ.
No lists of men held. NAM may have some, also copies of Regimental Magazine.

18TH (QUEEN MARY'S OWN) HUSSARS

Books
The Memoirs of the 18th (Queen Mary's Own) Royal Hussars 1906–22 Including
Operations in the Great War, Brigadier-General Chas. Burnett, Warren & Sons,
1926.
Museum
Cannon Hall Museum & Art Gallery, Cawthorne, Barnsley, S. Yorks S75 4AT.
No lists of men held.

19TH (QUEEN ALEXANDRA'S OWN ROYAL) HUSSARS

Books
No known books.

Museum
A Soldier's Life, Newcastle Discovery, Blandford House, Blandford Square, Newcastle-upon-Tyne NE1 4JA. (Mr Ralph Thompson)
Nominal Roll of the 19th Hussars Aug 1st 1914 (Call D.745); Registration Forms (D/9); Registration Forms NCOs 1908 (F/4).

20TH HUSSARS

Books
20th Hussars in the Great War, Major J.C. Dorling, published by the author, Lyndhurst, Hants., 1923.
Emperor's Chambermaids. The Story of the 14th/20th King's Hussars, Lieutenant-Colonel L.B.Oates, DSO.

Museum
Lancashire County & Regimental Museum, Stanley St., Preston, Lancs. PR1 4YP.
No lists of men held.

21ST (EMPRESS OF INDIA'S) LANCERS

Books
No known books.

Museum
Belvoir Castle, nr. Grantham, Lincs. NG33 7TJ.
No lists of men held.

THE SPECIAL RESERVE

The North Irish Horse
See 9th (North Irish Horse Bn.) Royal Irish Fusiliers.

The South Irish Horse
See 7th (South Irish Horse) Bn. Royal Irish Regiment.

King's Edward's Horse (The King's Overseas Dominions Regiment)
Corps Cavalry Regiment.

Yeomanry Regiments
See under English County Section and Wales, Ireland and Scotland.

10

ENGLISH REGIMENTS BY COUNTY

The following regiments, which have no obvious county association in their name, will be found under the county sections as follows.

The Border Regiment - Cumberland
The Sherwood Foresters - Derby and Notts
The Connaught Rangers - Ireland
The Buffs - Kent
The Queens's Own - Kent
The Sharpshooters - Kent
The King's Regiment - Lancashire
The Prince of Wales's Volunteers - Lancashire
The Inns of Court Rifles - London
The Royal Fusiliers - London
The King's Own Scottish Borderers - Northumberland
The Lovat's Scouts - Scotland
Prince Albert's - Somerset
The Queen's - Surrey
The Green Howards - Yorkshire
The King's Own - Yorkshire
Duke of Wellington's - Yorkshire (West Riding)
Prince of Wales's Own - Yorkshire (West Riding)
Isle of Man - see Cheshire
Rutland - see Leicestershire and Northamptonshire

BEDFORDSHIRE

Regiments
The Bedfordshire Regiment
The Bedfordshire Yeomanry

Books
The History of the Fifth Battalion, the Bedfordshire and Hertfordshire Regiment(TA), Captain F.A.M. Webster, Frederick Warne & Co. Ltd., 1930.
The 16th Foot. The History of the Beds and Herts Regiment, Major-General Sir F. Maurice, Constable & Co. Ltd., 1931.
The Story of the First—Fifth Bedfords, Edmund Rimmer, Manchester, 1917.

47

Natioal Roll of the Great War, Vols. 5 and 12 (IWM).
The Bedfordshire Yeomanry in the Great War, L.J.C. Southern, Rush & Warwick Ltd., 1935, 246 pp. Has a list of men who served.

Museum
Bedfordshire Regiment. Luton Museum, Wardown Park, Luton, Beds LU2 7HA. Has list of killed with place of death.
Bedfordshire Yeomanry. Bedford Museum, Castle Lane, Bedford MK40 3XD.

CRO
Records of the Beds and Herts Regiment are held, but these have only one short list of one platoon and TF Annual Camp 1913 Nominal Roll. (Ref: X550/1–5).
Tippetts(?) Directory for 1916 for Dunstable gives list of men serving.
List of those serving from Chalgrave (61 men) (Ref: P114/28/25 P.120–2)
Leighton Buzzard St. Andrews School (Ref: SD)
Marston School (Ref. SD)
Toddington(Ref:SD)
Bedford School Magazine (Ref: Z26/38).
Set of newspaper cuttings Beds Yeomanry (Ref: X344/163–4).
List of men serving in 90 out of 130 parishes; 11 of these 90 gave killed only (Ref: WV1/11).
List of teachers who served (Ref: EBV 14).
List of Boy Scouts from several districts.
Henlow Camp (Ref: Z50/142/108 and X498/178).
National Registration Local Tribunal – Non Appeal Tribunal Correspondence (a few names only).
Appeal Tribunal covered Beds, Hunts and Herts(?). Check other CRO
No other lists held.
Very good cross-indexes.
Several photographs.

Library
Not checked.

Other records
Bedfordshire FHS has a list of all who served from Gt. Barford.

BERKSHIRE

Regiments
Princess Charlotte of Wales's (The Royal Berkshire Regiment) The Berkshire Yeomanry The Berkshire Royal Horse Artillery

Books
The War Services of the 1/4 Royal Berkshire Regiment, C.R.M.F. Cruttwell, Basil Blackwell, 1922.

'D' Company 4th Battalion, The Royal Berkshire Regiment Aug 4 1914– 31 Oct 1928, Major A.C. Hughes and CSM A.Brant.

The Royal Berkshire Regiment (The Princess Charlotte of Wales) 49th – 66th Foot, Vols. 1 and 2, F. Loraine Petre, published at Reading, The Barracks.

List of Etonians who Fought in the Great War MCMXIV–MCMXIX, E.L. Vaughan, Riccardi Press, 1921.

The Yeomanry in Berkshire, Major G. Tilden, in the *Society for Army Historical Research Journal,* Vol. 28, 1950.

The Berkshire Yeomanry. 200 Years of Yeoman Service, A. Veney, A. French and S. Frost, Sutton Publishing, 1944. Copies available from the Berkshire Yeomanry Museum.

Berkshire Royal Horse Artillery 1914–19 G.F. Breach. Reprinted from The *Reading Standard,* 1923.

Museum

The museum of the modern Regiment. The Royal Berkshire and Wiltshire Regiment, The Wardrobe, 58 The Close, Salisbury SP1 2EX.

Has some records but these do not include complete lists of men.

The Royal Berkshire Yeomanry Cavalry Museum, TA Centre, Bolton Road, Windsor SL4 3JG.

Has a detailed day-by-day history of the Berkshire Yeomanry 1914–19 including indexes of soldiers' names, backgrounds and records of service, which are gradually being computerised. Current records are available for consultation via the Assistant Curator, A.G. French (Tel: 01491– 411308).

CRO

Report that they have no records.

The book *Berkshire and the War,* Vol. 1 1916, Vol. 2 1917, Vol. 3 1918, Vol. 4 1919, published by *The Reading Standard,* has a list of 8,000 names (1,004 pages).

Reading Reference Library has a manuscript index to the above. Also at Slough Reference Library and CRO, but these have no indexes. Entries often give photograph, unit, Battalion but no number.

Mrs. Rogers, 16 Springfield Road, Windsor, Berks SL4 3PQ also has a manuscript index.

BUCKINGHAMSHIRE

Regiments

The Oxfordshire and Buckinghamshire Light Infantry (see also Oxfordshire)

The Buckinghamshire Yeomanry (Royal Bucks Hussars)

Books

History of the 43rd and 52nd in the Great War, Captain J.E.H. Neville, Gale & Polden.

The 1st Bucks Battalion 1914—19, Captain P.L. Wright, Hazell, Watson & Viney Ltd., 1920. List of men. T

The 2nd Bucks Battalion 1914—18, J.C. Swann.

Citizen Soldiers of Buckinghamshire 1795—1926, J.C. Swann, Bucks TA Association, Hazell, Watson & Viney Ltd., 1930.

A Record of the 2nd Bucks Battalion TF 1914—18, TAVR Association, Bucks, Calton Press, Chesham.

The Oxford and Bucks Light Infantry Chronicle 1914—18, Vols. 24—27, A.F. Mockler-Ferryman.

The Local Community and the Great War. Aspects of Military Participation, I.F.W. Beckett, in *Records of Buckinghamshire,* Vol. XX, Part 4, 1978, pp.503—515.

Roll of Honour for Haddenham.

Museum
TA Centre, Slade Park, Headington, Oxford (Tel.01865-778479).

The museum has a card index covering many men of the Ox and Bucks from 1741 to 1958. They also have a few Regimental orders from 1914 to 1918 and a few Nominal Rolls from the Royal Bucks Hussars.

CRO
The CRO at Aylesbury has copies of the printed books as above.

With the Colours No.11 1918, the Journal of Hazell, Watson & Viney of Aylesbury, printers, gives list of employees who served (Ref: AR37/82).

Roll of Honour, of 19,500 Bucks men on active service. Alphabetically in pencil (Ref: TA/1/66Q). Volunteers before conscription.

Over 100 recruiting posters. (Hooker Collection)

Records of the TF Association.

Records of 1st and 2nd Bucks TF Bns., including orders.

Library
Not checked.

Other records
Bucks FHS Library. A list of 300 casualties, including wounded of the Royal Bucks Hussars.

CAMBRIDGESHIRE

Regiment
The Cambridgeshire Regiment

Books
The Cambridgeshires, 1914—19 Brigadier-General E. Riddell and Colonel M.C. Clayton, Bowes & Bowes, 1934.

The War List of the University of Cambridge 1914–18, G.V. Carey (Ed.), Cambridge University Press, 1921.
War Record of 1914–19 of the Cambridge University Press, (SOG).
Perse School Cambridge Roll of Honour 1914–18, (SOG).

Museums
Both the Blackburn Museum & Art Gallery, Museum St., Blackburn Lancs BB1 7AJ and the Lancashire County & Regimental Museum, Stanley St., Preston, Lancs. PR1 4YP include items about the old 30th (Cambridgeshire) Regiment which was the forerunner of the East Lancashire Regiment.

CRO
TF Minutes
Officers' Roll 1860–1929
Card Index of men of Cambridge in forces June 1915–July 1916.

Library
Cambridge University Library, University Archives.
The War List of the University of Cambridge 1914–18, G.V. Carey, Cambridge, 1921. (SOG)
Also check War List of King's College Cambridge 1914–18. (SOG)

CHESHIRE

Regiments
The Cheshire Regiment
The Cheshire Yeomanry (Earl of Chester's)

Books
The History of the Cheshire Regiment in the Great War, A. Crookenden; Chester printed by W.H. Evans, 1938. Lists killed and awards only.
The War Record of the 1/5th (Earl of Chester's) Battalion The Cheshire Regiment, August 1914–June 1919, Lieutenant-Colonel W.A.V. Churton, Phillipson & Golder, 1920 (CRO). Gives Nominal Roll 14th Feb 1915.
War History of the 6th Battalion the Cheshire Regiment (TF), Charles Smith, Stockport, 1932.
The Cheshire Yeomanry 1898–1967, Lieutenant-Colonel Sir R. Verdin, 1971 (CRO).
Chester in the Great War, by F.W. Longbottom, Phillipson & Golder. List of those from town who were killed. (Library)

Museum
The Castle, Chester CH1 2DN.
No lists of men held; some War Diaries.

CRO
Duke St., Chester CH1 1RL.
TF Minutes, accounts, general papers.
Draft of history of TF (2332/5).

Chester City Record Office
No Regimental records.
Staff of Bradley's (Chester) Ltd. CR108/1.
Also schools' rolls of honour: see *Chester Schools* by A.M. Kennett, 1973 from record office.
Records of the North West Military District, Welsh and Midland Command, and Western Command.
Sanitary Officers' Records 1904–14. Includes lists of infectious diseases, forms and general army orders for the district.

Library
St. John Street, Chester.
Has printed histories.
Short history of the 6th Cheshire Regiment. Typed Folio 35.5. No names.
Chester Corporation *Welcome Home Programme* names many men. Folio 35.5.
Nominal Roll of 1/5th Regiment in Jan 1915 in a large collection of newspaper cuttings. Folio 35.5.

ISLE OF MAN

Men from the Isle of Man fought with many Regiments but the Cheshire Regiment had a Manx Service Company.

Books
The Isle of Man and the Great War, B.E. Sargeaunt, Brown & Sons Ltd., 1920.
Roll of Honour, published by the *Isle of Man Times.*
Island at War. The Remarkable Role Played by the Small Manx Nation in the Great War 1914–18, Margery West, Western Book, Isle of Man. Includes those killed.
A History of the Manx Service Company and its Old Comrades Association, S.W. Corbett. (Ms. ref. MD913)

Museum
Douglas, Isle of Man.
Muster Roll of Isle of Man Volunteers 1846–1916. (MMM's 789C)
Roll Book of 2nd Manx Service Coy. (Cheshire Regiment), 1915. Also lists NCOs. (MMM's 887A)

CORNWALL

Regiment
The Duke of Cornwall's Light Infantry

Books
The History of the Duke of Cornwall's Light Infantry, Lieutenant N.H. Newey, Gale & Polden, 1924. Deals with the 2nd Bn. only.

The History of the Duke of Cornwall's Light Infantry 1914–19, E. Wyrall, Methuen, 1932. Lists awards and killed.

With the Cornwall Territorials on the Western Front, Lieutenant E.C. Matthews, 5th Bn. in the Great War, W.P. Spalding, 1921.

Museum
The Keep, Bodmin, Cornwall PL31 1EG.
Has a number of Nominal Rolls and other lists.
Enlistments Oct 1905–Aug 1914, Reg. Nos. 8184–10658; Aug–Sep 1914 10688–13181; Jun 1915–Mar 1916 22385–24901; Dec 1915–Oct 1916 25201–34240. Note the many gaps.
Nominal Roll of 3rd Bn. (Special Reserve) June 1908–July 1914.

CRO
  Truro
Records of County TF Association but no lists except Nominal Roll of NCOs and men of 573 (Cornwall) A.T. Coy RE Nov 1914–March 1919. (Ref: D.C/St.Austell-Fowey 215)
TF Attendance Book 1908–11.

CUMBERLAND AND WESTMORLAND

Regiments
The Border Regiment
The Westmorland and Cumberland Yeomanry

Books
The Border Regiment in the Great War, Colonel H.C. Wylly, Gale & Polden, 1924.
Records of the XI (Service) Battalion, Border Regiment, Lieutenant-Colonel P.W. Machell, J. Whitehead & Sons, 1916.
St. Bee's School Roll of Service 1914–19. (SOG)
No known book on the Yeomanry, but in 1917 the men were transferred to the 7th Bn. The Border Regiment.

Museum
The King's Own Royal Border Regiment, Queen Mary's Tower, The Castle, Carlisle CA3 8UR (Tel: 01228-32774). Contact the Curator, Mr S.A.Eastwood BA.AMA.
War Diaries 1st, 2nd, 2/4th, 5th, 6th, 7th, 8th, 9th and 10th Bns.: Rolls and Casualties details for 1st, 2nd, 2/4th, 6th, 7th & 11th Bns., some gallantry award details.
Army Lists; papers/diaries and information on some individual officers and men; maps; Commonwealth War Graves Commission Cemetery and Memorial locations for all officers, NCOs and men of the Border Regiment and Westmoreland & Cumberland Yeomanry.

CROs
Carlisle
Records of the Lonsdale Bn. (11th Border Regiment) Nominal Rolls 1916.
Pay and Mess Books, Employ Books 1914–16. Ref. D/LONS/L
Orders, Range Rolls, Railway Warrant Counterfoils.
Well-indexed archives of WW1/War Charities.
Carlisle City: Citizens League Minute Book.
War Memorial files, Workington.
War Pensions, Workington.
War Distress, Workington.
Military Service Tribunal, Penrith.
POWs in Germany, Penrith.
Military Service Tribunal, Whitehaven.
War Memorial, Whitehaven.
War Memorial, Cumwhinton.
War Distress, Scaleby.
Biographical notes on Lazonby's fallen.
Hodbarrow Mine: Millom men working in mine, on munitions and women in distress.
Carlisle YMCA Roll of Honour.
TF Association Cumberland and Westmoreland Yeomanry at Kendal.
Several diaries and photographs.
Several War Memorial Lists.
Roll of Honour, Corn Flour Mills, Silloth.
Barrow-in-Furness
Roll of Service of Barrow-in-Furness. Also gives those killed.
Kendal
See above.

DERBYSHIRE
See also Nottinghamshire

Regiments
The Sherwood Foresters (Nottinghamshire and Derbyshire Regiment)
The Derbyshire Yeomanry

Books
The 1st and 2nd Battalions The Sherwood Foresters (Nottinghamshire and Derbyshire Regiment) in the Great War, Colonel H.C. Wylly, Gale & Polden Ltd, 1924.

The Men from the Greenwood. Being the War History of the 11th (Service) Battalion Sherwood Foresters, Percy Fryer, Cresswell & Oakford, 1920.

Short History of the 16th Battalion The Sherwood Foresters (Chatsworth Rifles), Lieutenant-Colonel R.E. Truscott, Truscotts.

The Derbyshire Yeomanry War History: 1914–19, Lieutenant-Colonel G.A. Strutt, Bemrose & Sons Ltd, 1929.

Sherwood Foresters 1914–19, Captain W.C.C. Weetman, Thos. Forman & Sons, 1920.

The War History of the Fifth Battalion The Sherwood Foresters, Notts and Derby Regiment 1914–18, L.W. De Grave, Bemrose & Sons Ltd, 1930.

The Green Triangle. Being the history of the 2/5th Battalion, The Sherwood Foresters in the European War 1914–18, W.G. Hall, Garden City Press, 1920.

The Robin Hoods. 1/7th, 2/7th, 3/7th Bns. Sherwood Foresters 1914–18, Officers of the Battalion, Nottingham, J.& H. Bell, 1921.

6th Battalion The Sherwood Foresters 1914–18, Captain W.D. Jamieson, Chesterfield, 1958. (Museum)

The Sherwood Foresters in the Great War 1914–19. 1/8th Battalion, Captain W.C.C. Weetman MC, Thomas Forman & Sons, Nottingham, 1920.

The Sherwood Foresters in the Great War 1914–18. The 2nd/8th Battalion, by W.C. Oats, 1920.

Sherwood Foresters Yeomanry, Major H. Tallents, 1926. (Notts CRO)

Record of the Early Voluntary Movements and Notts Volunteer Regiment 1914–19, C. Gerring. (Notts CRO and Newark Library)

Museums
The Castle, Nottingham NG1 6EL.
War Diaries and printed histories as above.
RHQ Foresters House, Chetwynd Barracks, Chilwell, Nottingham NG9 5HA.
A database of 35,000 men.

CRO
Nottinghamshire
No lists of men held.
Derbyshire
No lists of men held.

Libraries
Angel Row, Nottingham
Not checked, but holds local collection.
Derby County Library
Printed books only.

Other records
St. Michael's Church, Breaston has a list of all who served from the Church.

DEVON

Regiments
The Devonshire Regiment
The Royal 1st Devon Yeomanry
The Royal North Devon Yeomanry

Books

The Devonshire Regiment 1914–18, C.T. Atkinson, Elan Bros, 1926. List of Casualties only.

Through Hell to Victory. From Passchendaele to Mons with the 2nd Battalion Devonshire Regiment in 1918, R.A. Colwill, Torquay, 1927. Diary of Lieutenant-Colonel Viscount Hambledon Sep 26 1915–Jan 4 1916 and Memorandum of the work of the Royal First Devon Yeomanry at Suvla Bay, W.H. Smith & Sons 1919.

The Yeomanry of Devon 1794–1927, Eng. Cmdr. Benson Freeman RN, The St. Catherine's Press, 1927.

Exwick during the Great War, A.H. Rousham.

Museums

The Devonshire Regiment

Military Museum of Devon & Dorset Regiment, The Keep Museum, Dorchester, Dorset DT1 1RN.

No lists of men held.

The Devon Yeomanry

Museum of North Devon, The Square, Barnstaple, N. Devon EX32 8LN.

The records of the Royal Devon Yeomanry are with their successors, D. Squadron (RDY) Wessex Yeomanry TAVR Centre, Oakleigh Road, Barnstaple, Devon.

CRO

Exeter

Printed books.

Rolls of Honour for Devon parishes and for Exeter City. It is unclear if these include all who served or only those killed. There are some lists within the files of the 500 parishes.

TF Association minutes.

Plymouth

No lists of men held.

Library

Plymouth Local History has no records.

DORSET

Regiments

The Dorsetshire Regiment

The Dorset Yeomanry (Queen's Own)

Books

The History of the Dorsetshire Regiment 1914–19, Part 1 Regular Bns., Part 2 TF Bns., Major H.O. Lock and O.C. Vidler, Part 3 The Service Bns., Regimental History Committee, Henry Ling Ltd, 1933. Lists killed and awards.

The Fine Fighting of the Dorsets: 1st Battalion The Dorset Regiment 1914–15, Major-General A.L. Ransome, Dorchester, 1959.

Records of the Dorset Yeomanry (Queen's Own) 1914–19, Major-General C.W. Thompson, F. Bennett & Co. Ltd., 1921. Lists of officers, men killed and awards.

Sherborne School. Old Shirburnian Navy and Army List 1914–19. (SOG)

Museums
    The Dorsetshire Regiment
    Military Museum of Devon & Dorset Regiment, The Keep Museum, Dorchester, Dorset DT1 1RN.
    No lists of men held.
    Dorset Yeomanry
    Contact Major L.E.N. Neville-Jones, c/o The Keep Museum.

CRO
    Dorchester
    An account of men of Rampisham who went to War 1914–18. (P.111/M111)

Other records
Iwerne Minster, J.H. Ismay. Life in the village during the War.

DURHAM
See also Northumberland

Regiment
The Durham Light Infantry

Books
Faithful. The Story of The Durham Light Infantry, S.G.P. Ward, 1962. Briefly covers WWI with maps and all DLI Battalions.

The Fifth Battalion The Durham Light Infantry 1914–18, Major A.L. Raimes, 1931. Based on War Diary. Roll of Honour. List of all officers and men serving in April 1915. Also includes a chapter on the 2/5th and 3/5th Battalions.

The Story of the 6th Battalion Durham Light Infantry. France, April 1915–Nov 1918, Captain R.B. Ainsworth, St. Catherine's Press, 1919. Lists officers died and officers' awards.

The Faithful Sixth. The History of the Sixth Battalion, The Durham Light Infantry, H. Moses. 1995. History of 6DLI 1860–1968. WWI Section based on War Diary.

8th Battalion The Durham Light Infantry 1793–1926, Major E.H. Veitch, J.H. Veitch & Sons, 1926. Based on War Diary. Rolls of Honour, Medals and chapters on POWs and 2/8th and 3/8th Battalions.

War History of the 18th (Service) Battalion Durham Light Infantry, Lieutenant-Colonel W.D. Lowe, Humphrey Milford, Oxford University Press, 1920. Based on War Diary. List of officers and medals.

The History of the Locally Raised 20th (Service) Battalion The Durham Light Infantry, Foreword by Lieutenant-Colonel K.J.W. Leatler, 1920. Roll of Honour and list of all who served before May 1916.

The Durham Forces in the Field 1914–18, Vol. 2, The Service Bns. of the Durham Light Infantry, Captain W. Miles. Cassell & Co. Ltd., 1920. The other volumes do not appear to be have been published.

The History of the Tyne Electrical Engineers, Royal Engineers 1884–1933, no imprint. (Durham University).

The History of the 3rd Durham Volunteer Artillery 1860 – 1960, Brigadier O.F.C. Hogg, South Shields, 1961.

The 142nd (Durham) Heavy Battery R.G.A. (T). Being a brief record of their work in France and Belgium, Major J.L. Marr, Rutter & King.

Hartlepools in the Great War. A record of Events 1914–19, Fred Miller.

Roll of Honour. West Hartlepool, Chas. A. Sage, 1920.

Museum

Aykley Heads, Durham DH1 5TU.
Medal Rolls (1977).
2nd Bn. War Diary and Field Returns (2221/1–4).
2nd Bn. Medal Awards (Vane Papers).
10th and 2nd Bns. Wounded 9th–10th Sep 1915. (Vane Papers)
9th Bn. War Diary and Field Returns (1500).
13th Bn. War Diary (2015).
20th Bn. History (796).
Large collection of papers with index to names.
Muster Rolls of TF 'F' Coy 6th Bn. June 1914 (2759).
Muster Rolls of TF 'D' Coy 8th Bn. Nov 1914 (2760/2).
15th Bn. Orders circa 1915 (99).

CRO

Durham

Men of Eaglescliffe who fought (EP/Eg 154).
Men of Bede College (E/HB/B56).

Libraries

Sunderland

Pease and Partners Ltd. (Darlington) Memoir 1914–18. Record of firm's employees killed in Service. Published 1920 with lists. Ref: 1940.3P.

War Records of Old Dunelmians, (Durham Public School) A.B. Thompson and E. Watts Moses (Eds.), 1914–19. L.920.042 T35 (Also Durham University Library).

See also *Sunderland Echo.*

Sunderland Polytechnic, Chester Road

Contact Mr. Peter H. Liddle B.A. 1914–18 Archives has very many records of personal diaries etc.

Newcastle Polytechnic
Has a very well-indexed newspaper cuttings library which covers from WWI to 1981 and is owned by Thompson Regional Newspapers.
Durham County Library, Framwellgate Bridge Road,
Not contacted.

ESSEX

Regiments
The Essex Regiment
The Essex Yeomanry

Books
Essex Units in the War, Vol. 1 1st Battalion The Essex Regiment, Vol. 2 2nd Battalion The Essex Regiment, Vol. 3 The Essex Yeomanry (Awards, Killed, Wounded), Vol. 4 Militia, Vol. 5 Essex Territorial Infantry Brigade (Awards), Vol. 6 Essex Regiment Service Battalions, J.W. Burrows.
A Short History of the 1st and 2nd Battalions The Essex Regiments, Gale & Polden, 1921. With the names of all those who laid down their lives for their Country 1914–18.
With the 1/5th Essex in the East, Lieutenant-Colonel T. Gibbons, Benham & Co. Ltd., 1921. (Awards, Killed, Wounded, POW, Officers).
The 10th Service Battalion Essex Regiment, Ban and Chell. (Chelmsford Museum)
Roll of Honour for Ilford.
The 10th (P.W.O.) Royal Hussars and the Essex Yeomanry during the European War 1914–18, Lieutenant-Colonel F.H.D.C. Whitmore, Benham & Co. Ltd., 1920. (Killed, Awards, Wounded, Officers)
Private Diary of Rev. Andrew Clark, Vicar of Great Leighs, North of Chelmsford, 92 volumes cover the period of the War giving details of life in the village. (Bodleian Library, Oxford) Few coincidental names.

Museum
Essex Regimental Museum, Oaklands Park, Moulsham Street, Chelmsford, Essex CM2 9AQ.
Has an index of over 100,000 Essex men of all units who served in the war. Will search in exchange for stamped, addressed envelope or 3 International Reply Coupons and discretionary donations to The Trustees of Essex Regimental Museum. One-Name study service available.

CRO
Waltham Forest
Printed Books
Minutes of Meetings of 3 Bn. C. Company (Hoe St): list of men present (W64E.R.V.T.2)
ditto Accounts also lists men. (W64ERVT4)

59

Southend
No lists of men held.
Chelmsford
Printed books only as above plus:
Alumni Felstedienses 1564–1931, F.S. Mollen. Old Felsteadian Society, London, 1931. War Service is noted.
Sons of Joyce Frankland, F. Thompson, (Newport Grammar School) Vol. 1, Old Newportian Society, 1979.
The History of Brentwood School, Brentwood, R.R. Lewis, Lists Honours. Newspaper cuttings T/Z43/2.
Halstead and Colne Valley Gazette, Fri. May 28, 1915. (Local newspaper) List of men serving from 48 parishes contains 2,600 names ("more next week"?)

GLOUCESTERSHIRE

Regiments
The Gloucestershire Regiment
The Gloucestershire Yeomanry (Royal Gloucestershire Hussars)
Books
The Gloucestershire Regiment in War 1914–18, Everard Wyrall, Methuen & Co. Ltd., 1931.
Infantry. An Account of the 1st Gloucestershire Regiment during the War 1914–18, Brigadier-General A.W. Pagan, Gale & Polden, 1951.
The Gloucestershire Regiment. War Narratives 1914–15, 1st and 2nd Battalions, Captain R.M. Grazebrook, The Regimental Association, 1927.
European War with the 5th Glosters at Home and Overseas from 3rd Aug 1914 to 21 March 1918, W.J. Wood, Crypt House Press Ltd., 1925.
The Fifth Gloucester Gazette, Gloucester, John Jennings, 1922. Reproduction from the original issues. Includes a roll.
The Story of the 2/5th Battalion Gloucestershire Regiment 1914–18, A.F. Burns (Ed.), The Crypt House Press Ltd., 1930. List of men.
The History of the Royal Gloucestershire Hussars Yeomanry, 1898–1922, Frank Fox, Philip Allen & Co., 1923.
Museum
Custom House, 31 Commercial Road, Gloucester GL1 2HE.
1/5th Glosters: Service Roll.
2nd Bn. orders 1907–27.
CROs
Bristol Record Office
List of Bristol men (with Regiment) and men of the Gloucester Regiment who were POWs. (Ref: 11177/5)

List of wounded soldiers entertained in Bristol 1917 (Ref: 11177/6).
Gallipoli Day report of reunion list 1915–18 (Ref: 19841/9).
Roll of Honour Bristol Corporation employees (Ref: 19841/8).

Gloucester Record Office
The Stroud District and its Part in the Great War 1914–19, Stroud News Publishing Co., c.1920. List of all men from district serving 1914–15.
Roll of Service, Alvington 1919 (P1ZSP1).
Roll of Honour, Blockley 1915 (P52MI9).
Roll of Service, Hucclecote 1915 (P183aPC4/8).
Roll of Honour, Tibberton 1918 (P332MI2).
Names of County Council employees on active service (CC/C1916A).

Libraries
  Bristol City
1/2 (City of Bristol) Volunteer Battalion the Gloucestershire Regt. Present members of the Battalion, Bristol, Edward Everard about 1918.
Souvenir and Roll of Honour of Bristol Officers, NCOs and men who had been awarded Decorations during the Great War, published by J. Arrowsmith, Bristol, 1919.
12th Gloucester Nominal Roll, June 1915.
Merchant Venturers Technical College Roll of Honour. J. Wright & Sons, Bristol, 1919. (Awards, Wounded, Killed).
Colstons School and the Great War 1914–18, H. Messenger, W. Bennett, 1923. Record of Service of Old Boys and Staff, 527 names, also list of killed. Photographs.
Bristol Roll of Honour, 1920. (Awards and Killed.)
Roll of Honour of Corporation Employees who served in H.M. Forces 1914–18. (Also Bristol and Avon FHS).

Other Records
John Lysaght Ltd., Bristol Engineering Firm. Men on service. 1450 names with unit. Bristol and Avon FHS.
W.D. and H.O. Wills Roll of Honour and War. Service Roll 1914–18. 1200 names with unit. Wills Library, Hartcliffe, Bristol.
List of Old Cheltonians and Masters who served in the War. (SOG).
Rolls are available in the following villages:
  Tytherington Roll of Honour; Newton St. Loe (in church); Corston (in church); Chew Magna/Chew Stoke, list of all men enlisting in 1914, few units; Freshford Memorial Hall, with units; Hirton Charterhouse, Memorial Hall, Milton. (Weston-Super-Mare) list of all enlisting 1914 with units.
1/5th Gloucester Roll April 1915. (Bristol and Avon FHS)
12th Gloucester Roll June 1915. (Bristol and Avon FHS and City Library)
South Midland Royal Engineers Nominal Roll, Dec 1914, Western Daily Press.

Dr. R.M. Pritchard, c/o Bristol and Avon FHS has a list and some details of 17,500 officers and men of the Gloucestershire Regiment, mostly extracted from local papers.

The information on Gloucestershire has been provided by two active genealogists who admit there must be a lot more sources hidden in villages.

HAMPSHIRE

Regiments

The Hampshire Regiment

The Hampshire Yeomanry (Caribiniers)

Books

Regimental History of the Royal Hampshire Regiment, Vols. 1 and 2, 1914–18, C.J. Atkinson, Glasgow, 1952. Awards and Officers. (CRO)

Some Account of the 10th and 12th Battalions The Hampshire Regiment 1914–18, Major W.S. Cowland (Ed.), Winchester, 1930.

Regimental Journal contains Roll of Honour and Casualty List for WWI.

History of the Hampshire Territorial Force Association and War Record of Units, 1914–19, Hampshire Advertiser Co. Ltd., Southampton, 1921.

Historical Records of the Hampshire Yeomanry Regiments, Lieutenant-Commander Benson Freeman RN, and similar titles.

Articles appearing in the *Hampshire Chronicle* starting July 1923; also in the *Hampshire Telegraph and Post* during 1925; also *Hampshire Advertiser and Independent* during 1925. See Portsmouth City Library.

Wykehamists Who Died in the War 1914–18, Vols. 1–4. Many photographs. (CRO)

National Roll of the Great War 1914–18, Section IV. Southampton, National Publishing Co. (Southampton City RO) Is not a complete list of all who served.

Portsmouth and the Great War, W.G. Gates (Ed.). (Portsmouth RO) Includes chapter on Hampshire Regiment.

Portsmouth Grammar School 1732–1976, E.S. Washington and A.J. Marsh. (Portsmouth RO)

Museum

The Royal Hampshire Regiment Museum and Memorial Garden, Serle's House, Southgate St., Winchester, Hampshire SO23 9EG.

No lists of men held.

CROs

Hampshire

Roll of Service of Sherborne St. John. (Ref: 14M72 PZ2)

There may be many others in parish collections.

Portsmouth

Victoria Road, North Boys Secondary School. (Ref.: 79A/2 and 781A/2/7)

United Breweries, Portsmouth. (Ref.: 412A/7/83)
Portsmouth Branch of Old Contemptibles Association. (Ref.: 942A/1)
Photographs of the Wessex Brigade.

Southampton
No lists of men held.

Isle of Wight
No lists of men held.

Libraries
Not contacted, but Portsmouth Central has printed books and local newspapers.

Other records
Abbots Ann near Andover has plaque in War Memorial Hall naming all who served.
Headley. A list of men in forces 1915 and 1918 is available in the Guildford CRO.
    (PSH/HED/22/7–8)

HEREFORDSHIRE

Regiment
The Herefordshire Regiment

Books
Historical Record of the Herefordshire Light Infantry and its Predecessors, G.
    Archer Parfitt (Ed.), Hereford, 1962.
Manu Forti, Lieutenant-Colonel Hill, published by Suttons.
The Regiment and a few of its men are also mentioned in the following:
Military Operations in Gallipoli, Peter Ashton.
History of the 53rd Welsh Division 1914–18, Peter Ashton.
The Advance of the Egyptian Expeditionary Force 1917–18, Peter Ashton.

Museum
c/o 'C' Coy. 5th Bn. The Light Infantry (TA), TA Centre, Harold St., Hereford.
Roll Book, 'A' Coy, 1/1st Herefordshire Regiment
Some Post War Battalion Rolls.
Photographs and Roll of Honour.
List of old Hereford Rifle Volunteer Company of pre-1908.

CRO
    Hereford
TA Minute Books.

Library
Hereford City may have copies of local newspapers.

HERTFORDSHIRE

Regiments

The Hertfordshire Regiment

The Hertfordshire Yeomanry

Books

The 16th Foot. A History of the Beds and Herts Regiment, Major-General Sir F. Maurice, Constable & Co. Ltd., 1931.

A Brief Record of the Herts Yeomanry and the Herts Artillery, Major A.L.P. Griffith, Geo. Creasy & Sons, 1927.

Hertfordshire's Soldiers, J.D. Sainsbury, Hertfordshire Local History Council, 1969.

A Record of Honours and Awards to Officers and Men of the Herts Yeomanry and Artillery Unit, Hertfordshire Yeomanry and Artillery Historical Trust, c/o Major J.D. Sainsbury, 8 Mornington, Digswell, Welwyn, Herts. AL6 0AJ.

In Memoriam and Roll of Honour, Hatfield.

Watford Grammar School Book of Remembrance. (SOG)

Museums

The Hertfordshire Regiment

Hertford Museum, 18 Bull Plain, Hertford SG14 1DT.

No lists of men held except for a few pre-war rolls of Yeomanry and Artillery.

The Hertfordshire Yeomanry

Barnet Museum.

List of Congregational Church (Wood St.) members with 120 photographs. Index. London and North Middlesex FHS.

CRO

Hertford

List of men serving from Willian. (D/P 125/29/4)

Orders at Gaza.

TF Association Minutes.

Old Boys from Herts Reformatory School, Chapmore End, Bengeo who served. (D/E Hts Q82)

Casualty Records, Yeomanry and Artillery Units. (D/E Y0 2/11, D/E Y0 2/19)

Kings Walden, List of Men serving. (D/P 112 29/2)

Admissions and Discharge Book and photographs for Australian Auxiliary Hospital, Digswell.

War Memorial Committee Records. (D/P34 29/1–D/P34 29/10).

List of men in Aldenham (D/P3 1/17).

Libraries

Cheshunt, Letchworth, Hitchin, St. Albans and Watford.

Not checked.

Other records
Bishop Stortford School Roll of Honour. (SOG)
Shephall Parish, near Stevenage. Order of Service lists all who served (see Fig. 1).

HUNTINGDON AND PETERBOROUGH

Regiments
The Huntingdonshire Cyclist Battalion

Books
None found.

Museum
None known.

CRO
Huntingdon RO has a list of men from Huntingdon who served.
No other records.

Other records
Mayor of Peterborough's list of Peterborough men who served. Copy in Peterborough Museum.

ISLE OF MAN

See Cheshire.

KENT

Regiments
The Buffs (East Kent Regiment)
The Queen's Own (Royal West Kent Regiment)
Royal East Kent Yeomanry (Duke of Connaught's Own)
The West Kent Yeomanry (Queen's Own)
Kent and Sharpshooters Yeomanry
The Kent Cyclist Battalion

Books
Historical Records of the Buffs, East Kent Regiment, Vol. 3, 1914–19, Colonel R.S. Moody, The Medici Society, 1922.

The Queen's Own Royal West Kent Regiment 1914–19, C.T. Atkinson, Simpkin, Marshall & Hamilton, Kent & Co. Ltd, 1924. (Awards)

Invicta. With the 1st Battalion Queen's Own Royal West Kent Regiment in the Great War, Major C.V. Molony, Nisbet & Co. Ltd., 1923. (Awards and 'Special Acts of Gallantry')

History of the 8th Battalion Queen's Own Royal West Kent Regiment, Lieutenant-Colonel H.J. Wenyon and Major H.S. Brown, Hazell Watson & Vinery, 1921. (Awards)

History of the 11th (Lewisham) Battalion Queen's Own Royal West Kent Regiment, R.O. Russell, Lewisham Newspaper Co. Ltd., 1934. (All who served.)

Queen's Own Gazette 1914–23, contains promotions, wounded, etc.

Invicta Gazette, Journal of 20th Bn. London Regiment 1916–17 (was part of QORWKR).

All the above are in the Kent CRO, Maidstone.

West Kent (Q.O.) Yeomanry and the 10th (Yeomanry) Battalion, The Buffs 1914–19, Lieutenant-Colonel Charles Ponsonby, Andrew Melrose Ltd., 1920.

Kent Fencibles. Nov 1915–July 1918. (Bromley Library)

The Sharpshooters, 3rd County of London Yeomanry 1900–61, Boris Mollo Historical Research Unit, c.1970. Lists companies.

The Kent Cyclist Battalion. A History of the Kent Cyclist Battalion TF 1908–20, and *Kent Cyclist Battalion,* both by Cyril Bristow, 11 Knowsley Way, Hildenborough Tonbridge, Kent TN11 9LG. Taken from five separate sources, including the Regimental magazines and all known Nominal Rolls. Name Indexes. Copies at Kent Archive Office, Maidstone.

Also check *The Kent Bibliography and Supplement, 1977,* a finding aid for Kent Material in Public Libraries of Kent and SE London, published by the Library Association, London and Home Counties Branch.

Museums

Queen's Own (Royal West Kent Regiment)
Regimental Museum, Maidstone Museum & Art Gallery, St. Faith's St., Maidstone Kent ME14 1LH.

The Princess of Wales's Royal Regiment and Queen's Regiment
Inner Bailey, Dover Castle, Kent CT16 1HU.
All records with Kent CRO.

The Buffs
The Royal Museum, 18 High Street, Canterbury, CT1 2JE.

Kent and Sharpshooters Yeomanry
Hever Castle, near Edenbridge, Kent TN8 7NG.
All records with National Army Museum.

The Kent Cyclist Battalion
Maidstone Museum & Art Gallery, St. Faith's St., Maidstone, Kent ME14 1LH. Records held at Kent Archive Office, Maidstone. Printed books with name lists photographs, etc.

CRO

Kent CRO, Maidstone
Holds records of East Kent Yeomanry and QORWKR. These include
Nominal Roll 8th Bn. QORWKR, 2 volumes, 1915–19. (Ref.: WKR/B8/A5).
Ditto, 1 file 1918. (Ref.: WKR/B8/A6)
Notes on Honours 1914–18. (Ref.: WKR/BZ/Z24)

Nominal Roll B Coy 1917, 1 volume. (Ref.: WKR/B6/AZ)
Nominal Roll No. 9 Section 1917. (Ref.: WKR/B6/A3)
5th Bn. Standing Orders 1914–16. (Ref.: WKR/ADDH/B2/5/A2)
Kent S.E. Folkestone
Index cards used for compilation of Roll of Honour. (Ref.: FO/AC6/5/1)
Libraries
Grace Hill Reference Library, Folkestone.
Printed War Service of Dover College.
Local Newspapers which contain lists of men.
Regimental Histories of The Buffs and QORWKR.
Bexley, London
Holds most of the printed books.
Bromley, London
Holds most of the printed books.
Lewisham, London
Holds most of the printed books.

Other records
Tonbridge School and the Great War 1914–18, The Whitefriars Press Ltd., 1923. (SOG)
St. Mary Cray Council School, Orpington. (Kent FHS and IWM)
Coye's Grammar School, Lewisham and the Great War 1914–19, L.L. Duncan, The Blackheath Press, 1920. (Lewisham Library)
Kings School Canterbury Register 1859–1931. (Canterbury Cathedral Archives)
Hartlip parish has a list in Church porch.
Birling. A Backward Glance, Margaret Collins, Brian Collins, 1982. Has a four page list of all who served from this Kent village.

LANCASHIRE

Regiments
The Lancashire Fusiliers
The King's Own (Royal Lancaster Regiment)
The Prince of Wales's Volunteers (South Lancashire Regiment)
The Loyal North Lancashire Regiment
The East Lancashire Regiment
The King's (Liverpool Regiment)
8th Bn. the Liverpool Irish & 10th Bn. the Liverpool Scottish)
The Manchester Regiment
The Lancashire Hussars Yeomanry
Duke of Lancaster's Own Yeomanry

Books

The History of the Lancashire Fusiliers 1914–18, Vols. 1 and 2, Major-General J.C. Latter, Gale & Polden, 1949. No lists but index to many names.

The Royal Fusiliers. The Roll of Honour of the Salford Brigade (15th, 16th, 19th, 20th, 21st) Lancashire Fusiliers, Sir C.A. Montague Barlow, Sherratt & Hughes, 1919.

The Lancashire Fusiliers Annual, Major B. Smyth (Ed.), Nos. 1–36 1891–1926.

The History of the 2/6th Lancashire Fusiliers. The story of a 2nd line Territorial Battalion 1914–19, Captain C.H. Potter and Captain A.S.C. Fothergill, Rochdale Observer, 1927.

The Salford Pals. A History of the 15th, 16th, 17th and 20th Bns. Lancashire Fusiliers, Michael Steadman, Leo Cooper 1993.

At Ypres with Bert Dunkley, Thomas H. Floyd, John Lane, 1920. Covers 2/5th Lancashire Fusiliers.

The King's Own. The Story of a Regiment, Vol.3 1914–50, Colonel J.M. Cowper, Gale & Polden, 1957.

The Fourth Battalion The King's Own (Royal Lancaster) Regiment and the Great War, Lieutenant-Colonel W.F.A. Wadham and Captain J. Crossley, Crowther & Goodman, 1935. Copies available from Museum.

The King's Own TF. Being a Record of the 1/5th Battalion of the King's Own (Royal Lancaster) Regiment in the European War 1914–18, Captain A. Hodgkinson. Lewis Press, 1921.

The History of the 89th Brigade 1914–18. 17th–20th Battalions The King's, Brigadier-General F.G. Stanley, Liverpool: Daily Post, 1919.

Ich Dien. The Prince of Wales Volunteers (South Lancashire) 1914–34, Captain H Whalley Kelly, Gale & Polden Ltd 1935.

The South Lancashire Regiment (Prince of Wales Volunteers), Colonel B.R. Mullaly White Swan Press. Bristol 1952.

The Loyal (North Lancashire) Regiment, Vols. 1 and 2, Colonel H.C. Wylly, The United Services Institute, 1932.

War History of the 1st/4th Battalion The Royal North Lancashire Regiment, now the Loyal Regiment 1914–18, Geo. Toulmin & Sons Ltd, Preston, 1921. Includes list of awards, casualties and volunteers of 1914.

Spectamur Agendo. 1st Battalion, The East Lancashire Regiment Aug and Sep 1914, Captain E.C. Hopman, Heffer, 1926.

The History of the East Lancashire Regiment in the Great War 1914–18, Major-General Sir Lothian Nicholson and Major H.T. McMullen, Littlebury, 1936.

First Battalion The East Lancashire Regiment, Soar Plebiscite.

The Accrington Pals. The 11th (Service) Battalion (Accrington) East Lancashire Regiment. A Pictorial History, William Turner, published by Accrington Library

The Story of the King's (Liverpool) Regiment formerly the 8th Foot, T.R. Threlfall Country Life, London, 1916. (List of officers.)

APPENDIX III.

NOMINAL ROLL.

NOTE.—This Roll has been compiled from the battalion's Part II Orders, and though every effort has been taken to make it accurate, the author feels that for various reasons—in particular the somewhat scanty records of the early period of 1914–15— some errors of fact and date may be present. It is hoped that, as some 4,000 names are recorded, those who suffer from inaccuracies will accept in extenuation the magnitude of the task.

It had been intended to give, where applicable, some record of service done with other units, but it has been found impossible to obtain a complete record of this, and the Roll in consequence is confined to details of service, distinctions, etc., in the battalion. This restriction is the more to be regretted as so many members of the battalion gained high rank and honours with other units, among them being Rifleman G. G. Coury, who shortly after obtaining his commission won the Victoria Cross.

A ✝ has been placed against the name of every officer and man who was killed in action or died of wounds or disease.

THE HISTORY
of the
2/6th (Rifle) Battalion "The King's"
(Liverpool Regiment)
1914-1919

BY
CAPT. C. E. WURTZBURG, M.C.
Adjutant, Nov. 1916-Nov. 1918

WITH A FOREWORD BY
MAJOR-GENERAL SIR R. W. R. BARNES, K.C.B., D.S.O.
Late G.O.C. 57th (West Lancs.) Division

PRINTED FOR THE REGIMENTAL COMMITTEE
BY
GALE & POLDEN LIMITED
WELLINGTON WORKS, ALDERSHOT
1920

Fig. 3. An extract from a Battalion History which includes a Nominal Roll of all who served. The preamble to the list of names indicates the problems in compiling a complete list even in 1920. Reproduced with permission of the publishers, The King's Regiment.

69

The History of the King's Regiment (Liverpool) 1914–19, Vols. 1–3, Everard Wyrall, Edward Arnold & Co., 1928–35.

The History of the 2/6th (Rifle) Battalion, The Kings (Liverpool Regiment) 1914–19, Captain C.E. Wurtzburg, The Regimental Committee, Gale & Polden. (Contains 4000 names which it is hoped includes every man who served.)

The Liverpool Scottish 1900–19, A.M. MacGilchrist, 1/10 and 2/10 Kings, Henry Young, 1930. (Awards, Roll of Honour, Nominal Roll 1st Bn. 1st Nov 1914.)

The Record of the 11th Battalion of The King's (Liverpool) Regiment, subsequently the 15th Battalion of the Loyal North Lancashire Regiment Pioneers, 14th Light Division. Aug 1914–March 1919, R.E. Thomas & Co., 1920.

The History of the Manchester Regiment (late 63rd and 96th Foot), Vols. 1 and 2, Colonel H.C. Wylly, Forster Groom & Co. Ltd., 1923–25.

The Manchesters, Captain G.L. Campbell. A History of the Regular, Militia, Special Reserve, Territorial and New Army Battalions since their formation, London Picture Advertising Co. Ltd., 1916. (List of officers, casualties and awards.)

Sixteenth, Seventeenth, Eighteenth, Nineteenth Battalions The Manchester Regiment (1st City Brigade), A record 1914–18, Sherratt & Hughes., 1923.

The Seventh Manchester, July '16–March '19, Captain S.J. Wilson, Manchester University Press, 1920.

Manchester City Battalions of the 90th and 91st Infantry Brigade. Book of Honour, Brigadier-General F. Kempster and Brigadier-General H.C.E. Westropp, Sherratt & Hughes, 1917. (Lists all men in the 16th, 17th, 18th, 19th, 20th, 21st, 22nd and 23rd Bns. Also listed by firms.)

The 21st Battalion of the Manchester Regiment. A History by a Committee of Old Members of the Regiment, Sherratt & Hughes, 1934.

The Oldham Battalion of Comrades (24th Battalion Manchester Regiment) Book of Honour, Alderman Herbert Wilde, Sherratt & Hughes.

The 42nd (East Lancashire) Division 1914–18, F.P. Gibbon, Country Life, London, 1920. (Awards only.)

The Story of the 55th Division 1916–19, J.O. Coop, Liverpool, 1919. (Officers only)

A History of the East Lancashire Royal Engineers, Members of the Corps, Country Life, London, 1921. (Awards)

The Bolton Artillery. A History 1860–1975, A.J. Wingfield, 1976.

History of the Bolton Artillery 1860–1928, Lieutenant-Colonel B. Palin Dobson, Blackshaw, Sykes & Morris Ltd., 1929. (Awards)

The Story of the 63rd Field Ambulance. (2/2 West Lancashire Field Ambulance TF) 1914–19, A.W. Westmore, M. Thomson and J.E. Allison, Wood & Sloane Ltd., 1928.

History of the 2/3rd East Lancashire Field Ambulance. The Story of a 2nd line TF Unit 1914–19, Alfred E.F. Francis, W.F. Jackson & Sons, 1930.

Lancashire Territorials in Gallipoli, G. Bigwell, London, 1916. (Awards). (CRO Preston).

Hell's Foundations. A Town, its Myths and Gallipoli, Geoffrey Moorhouse. Hodder & Stoughton, 1992.
Duke of Lancaster's Own Yeomanry - none found.

Museums

Lancashire Fusiliers
The Fusiliers Museum, Lancashire, Wellington Barracks, Bury, Lancs. BL8 2PL.
Enlistment Book 1881–1903.
May be a few Bn. orders etc.
No lists.

King's Own (Royal Lancaster) Regiment
City Museum, Market Square, Lancaster, Lancs. LA1 1HT.
Copies of War Diaries and partial Muster Rolls.
On-going computerised indexed lists of men, officers and awards.
The archivist is happy to deal with family history enquiries but by telephone first (01524-6463) for an appointment.

The Prince of Wales's Volunteers (South Lancashire Regiment)
Lancashire County & Regimental Museum, Stanley St., Preston, Lancs. PR1 4YP.
A set of War Diaries.
List of all who passed through the 3rd Bn., mainly recruits and wounded.
No TF recruits.

The Loyal North Lancashire Regiment
Regimental Museum, Queen's Lancashire Regiment, Fulwood Barracks, Preston, Lancs. PR2 4AA.
No lists of men held.

East Lancashire Regiment
Blackburn Museum & Art Gallery, Museum St., Blackburn, Lancs. BB1 7AJ.
No lists of men held.
Towneley Hall, Burnley, Lancs. BB11 3RQ.
Lancashire County & Regimental Museum, Stanley St., Preston, Lancs. PR1 4YP.

The King's (Liverpool Regiment)
Liverpool Museum, William Brown Museum, Liverpool L3 8EN.
No lists of men held.

Liverpool Scottish
Forbes House, Score Lane, Liverpool L16 6AN.
Roll of Y Coy, 1914–19.
Details of casualties at Hooge.
Scrap books of cuttings.
Liverpool Scottish Journal gives promotions and attestments.
Orders 2/10 Bn. 1915.
Photographs
Personal diaries.

Acc. No. 29 Numerical Roll 6500 names out of 10,000 who served 1914—18.
Acc. No. 32 Attestment Book 1915.
Acc. No. 19 Draft Book. Rolls of 1st 32 drafts going to France.
Nominal Roll of those paying for Highland Dress 1914—16.

The Manchester Regiment
Museum of the Manchesters, Ashton Town Hall, Ashton-under-Lyne OL6 6DL.

Duke of Lancaster's Own Yeomanry
Lancashire County & Regimental Museum, Stanley St., Preston, Lancs. PR1 4YP.
No lists of men held.

CRO
Salford City Archives
No lists of men held.

Liverpool University Archives
Diary of Charles A. Wells.
Roll of Service Aug '14—Nov '18, Liverpool U.P., 1921. Lists both staff and graduates
of University.
Lancashire Biographies, Rolls of Honour, W. Ralph Hall Caine, Richard J. James,
1917.
The University Roll of Honour (War Service) is on pages 424—450 of the above
book; also includes Liverpool College, Manchester Grammar School, Merchant
Taylors School, Rossall School and Lancaster Royal Grammar School.

Lancashire CRO, Preston
Printed books.
No manuscript records listed.

Libraries
Bolton Reference Library..
Printed books.
The Boltonian This magazine of Bolton School gives lists of old boys on active
service with limited details of unit.
Index of biographies of soldiers printed in *Bolton Journal.*

Liverpool City Library
Large collection of obituaries and newspaper cuttings relating to the War period.
Records of 55th Division.
Records of 2nd Volunteer Bn. The King's Regiment (includes list of men serving).
Printed histories.
Local newspaper.
May have other records as no full search was made.

Salford Local Library
Printed books (The Lancashire Fusiliers; Manchester City Bns.)
Local newspapers.

Mather and Platt Ltd. (Park Works, Salford Iron Works, Boiler Yard). *A Record of the Part Taken by all Employees During the Great War 1914–19.* London Office and Branch Offices at Home and Overseas.

Other records
Warrington Guardian Year Book and Almanac for 1920, contains Warrington's part in the War and a 15-page Roll of Honour.

LEICESTERSHIRE

Regiments
The Leicestershire Regiment
The Leicestershire Yeomanry (Prince Albert's Own)

Books
The History of the 1st and 2nd Battalions The Leicestershire Regiments in the Great War Colonel H.C. Wylly, Gale & Polden, 1928.
Footprints of the 1/4th Leicestershire Regiment Aug 1914–Nov 1918 Captain John Milne, Edgar Bachus, 1935.
The Fifth Leicester. A Record of the 1/5th Battalion The Leicester Regiment Territorial Force during the War 1914–19 Captain J.D. Hills, The Echo Press, 1919. (CRO)
An Outline of the History of The Leicestershire (Prince Albert's Own) Yeomanry, Colonel G.R. Codrington, W.H. Smith & Son, 1928; Eyre & Spottiswoode, 1955. (Leicestershire CRO)
Leicester 1914–18, F.P. Armitage. The war-time story of a Midland Town. (CRO)

Museum
c/o Leicester City Council, Newarke House Museum, The Newarke, Leicester LE2 7BY.
    Has a collection of Bn. Rolls of Honour, a regimental names list and a set of printed books of the Regiment.
Old Comrades Association Members list.
Also medals.
Rest of records in CRO.

CRO
57 New Walk, Leicester.
Printed books as above.
Set of War Diaries and other note books (Ref.: 22D63/130–254); see Index DE 407/1–78.
Records of Leicester War Records Society. (14D35)
Records of POWs Leicestershire and Rutland (22D61).
Leicester Roll of Honour. (15D40)
Records of Leicester Old Contemptibles 1958–76.

73

Records of Hinckley War Relief Committee. (DE1961)
Letters of RK Pears. (DE 2051/6–9)
List of Old Lindleians. (DG 38/13)
Miscellaneous papers WWI. (DE 836/36)
Letters from Italy. (DE 1061/21)
Photographs in Hospital. (DE 2381/18–20)
Letters Misc. 628.
TF Association Minutes, A/c books and records.

Other records
Old Uppingham School Roll of Honour. (SOG)

LINCOLNSHIRE

Regiments
The Lincolnshire Regiment
The Lincolnshire Yeomanry

Books
The History of the Lincolnshire Regiment 1914–18, Major-General C.R. Simpson. Medici Society, 1931.
The History of the 10th Foot 1914–1915, Major L.C. Gates, Gale & Polden, 1953.
History of the 5th Battalion The Lincolnshire Regiment, Colonel T.E. Sandall, Basil Blackwell, 1922.
The 8th (S) Battalion Lincolnshire Regiment 1914–18, Gale & Polden 1919.

Museum
Museum of Lincolnshire Life, Old Barracks, Burton Road, Lincoln LN1 3LY.
  Lincolnshire Regiment
Embarkation Lists, 1st Battalion 1914.
1914 Star Medal Roll, 2nd Battalion.
Battalion War Diaries (indexed). No individual service records held.
Lincolnshire Yeomanry: Lists of men 1914; some documents in private hands. Some pre-1914 records.
  Spalding Museum
No lists of men held.

CRO
  The Castle, Lincoln
TF Association Minutes and A/cs. War Diaries. May be lists in some parish records.
  Humberside RO Grimsby
Scunthorpe Urban District Roll of Honour Aug 1914–Oct 1917. (Men serving with some photographs). (518/5/3)

Libraries
Lincoln City Library holds local collection. Not checked.

LONDON AND MIDDLESEX

Regiments

The Duke of Cambridge's Own Middlesex Regiment

The London Regiment. The city's Territorial Force regiment. Consisted of: The Royal Fusiliers, London Rifle Brigade, Post Office Rifles, Queen Victoria's Rifles, Finsbury Rifles, The Rangers, London Scottish, Prince of Wales's Own Civil Service Rifles, Queen's Westminster Rifles, Poplar and Stepney Rifles, London Irish Rifles, First Surrey Rifles, The Queen's, Cyclists Battalion and Artists Rifles.

The City of London Yeomanry (Roughriders)

1st County of London Yeomanry (Middlesex. Duke of Cambridge's Hussars)

2nd County of London Yeomanry (Westminster Dragoons)

3rd County of London Yeomanry (Sharpshooters) (see Kent)

The National Guard

The Inns of Court Officer Training Corps

Books

The Die-hards in the Great War: A History of the Duke of Cambridge's Own (Middlesex Regiment) 1914–19, Vols. 1 and 2, Everard Wyrall, Harrison & Sons Ltd., 1926–30.

The History of the 7th Battalion Middlesex Regiment, Colonel E.J. King, Harrison & Sons Ltd., 1927. List of officers (Haringey).

The 16th Public Schools Battalion Middlesex Regiment and the Great War, 1914–18, H.W. Wallisgrain, London, 1935.

The City of London Yeomanry (Roughriders), A.S. Hamilton, The Hamilton Press Ltd., 1936.

2nd County of London (Westminster Dragoons) Yeomanry, Major Edward Rowe, Wm. Clowes & Sons Ltd., 1962.

Historical Records of the Middlesex Yeomanry 1797–1927, Charles Stonham and Benson Freeman, Regimental Committee, 1930 (Middlesex Yeomanry Museum). Lists some names.

The Yarn of a Yeoman, S.F. Hatton, Hutchinson & Co. Ltd., 1930.

The London Regiment was formed in 1908 and consisted of 26 Territorial Force Bns. The 26th and 27th were allocated to the Honourable Artillery Coy. and the Inns of Court Volunteer Rifle Corps. Neither of these famous units joined the Regiment and the two Bn. Nos. were never re-allocated. In July 1916 the 26 Bns. were allocated to other Regiments, so that reference should also be made to: Surrey, Royal Fusiliers, Kent, Middlesex, The King's Royal Rifle Corps and The Rifle Brigade. There is no general history of the London Regiment but A.S. White lists about 40 books dealing with the 26 separate Bns. The London Regiment formed a total of 62 Service Bns. and 26 Reserve Units during the war.

The Royal Fusiliers in the Great War, H.C. O'Neill, Wm. Heinemann, 1922.

The History of the Old 2/4th (City of London) Battalion of the London Regiment (Royal Fusiliers), Colonel F.W. Walker, Westminster Press, 1919. List of all who served.

The 23rd (Service) Battalion RF (1st Sportsman's). A Record of Service 1914–19, Fred W. Ward, Sedgwick & Jackson, 1920. Part Nominal Roll.

Cannon Fodder. An Infantryman's Life on the Western Front 1914–18, A. Stuart Dolden, 1st Bn. London Scottish.

The History of the Post Office Rifles, Charles Messenger. 170pp.

The History of the London Rifle Brigade 1859–1919 (1921). The London Rifle Brigade was the 5th (City of London) Bn., The London Regiment.

The Second Twentieth, being the History of the 2/20th Battalion London Regiment, Captain W.R. Elliot, MC, Gale & Polden, 1920. Warrant Officers and Sergeants listed. (Lewisham Library)

History of Queen Victoria's Rifles, C.A.G. Keeson. (QVR Museum).

Twice in a Lifetime, M.L. Walkinton, Samson Books, 1983. The story of one man's service in the Queen's Westminster Rifles.

The Story of Lee, F. Gregory and F.W. Nunn. Lee was an ASC training depot in WWI. Has lists of names.

Grove Park in the Great War, John King, July 1983, Grove Park Community Group. Grove Park was another ASC training depot in WWI.

The National Guard in the Great War 1914–18, A.E. Manning Foster, Cope & Fenwick, 1920. The London TF Association controlled the National Guard and also very many 'non-infantry' units allocated to the various Corps, e.g. RAMC, RE, RFA, etc.

Museums

Middlesex Yeomanry

Royal Corps of Signals Museum, Blandford, Dorset.
Lists nearly all who served in 1914. Some records up to the end of the war but deteriorate after 1917. Check records of Benson Freeman in IWM or NAM.

Inns of Court and City Yeomanry

10 Stone Buildings, Lincoln's Inn, London WC2A 3TG
Has a copy of a book: *The Inns of Court Officers' Training Corps during the Great War*, Lieutenant-Colonel F.H.L. Errington, Printing-Craft Ltd., 1922. This has a complete list of all who passed through the unit as well as permanent staff.
Also has a copy of *The City of London Yeomanry (Roughriders)*.
No other lists.

London Scottish Regiment RHQ

95 Horseferry Road, London SW1P 2DX.
Has a list of men from all 3 Bns.

City of London (Royal Fusiliers)

HM Tower of London EC3N 4AB.

No lists but some of the many printed books have complete lists of all who served. A few Bn. orders, photographs, etc.
Journal of Orders and Medals Research Society, Autumn 1976, has an article on the Regimental. Nos. of the Artists Rifles (28th Bn.).

Queen Victoria's Rifles Regimental Association
56 Davis St., London W1 (but museum no longer in existence).
List of missing, July—Oct 1918 all London Regiment Bns. List of Officers. Selection of printed books of the Bn. and the London Regiment.
Some pre-war muster rolls, diaries and notes.
Most records lost in 1939—45 war (HQ bombed 1941).
Keeson's history of the regiment is now held by the Hon. Sec., N.D. Humerstone.

Libraries
Westminster Library
160 Buckingham Palace Rd.
Photographs of Westminster Volunteers (13th Middx).
Archives of Watney, Combe, Reid & Co. Ltd. Brewers include list of men serving. (Acc. No. 789)
Archives of Harrison and Sons Ltd. Printers lists apprentices who were in Forces. (Acc. No. 1272)
Archives of St. Michael, Chester Sq. have list of men who returned. (Acc. No. 1320)

Lambeth
52 Knatchbull Road.
London and Surrey Regiments. Printed books. Bn. orders and list of recruits 1914 (Ref.: IV/36/1/15) of 1st Surrey Rifles. (21st Bn.).
Roll of Service, Gipsy Rd. School, Norwood.
See Surrey entry.

Hammersmith and Fulham
No lists of men held.

Hackney and Rose Lyman
No lists of men held.

Lewisham
Printed books Kent and London Regiments. See Kent entry.

Haringey
Bruce Castle Museum. Admission Registers for 1st Volunteer Bn., Middx. Regiment gives names of men who transferred to Regulars. Printed books.

Society of Genealogists' Library
Many Rolls of Honour (most listed in this book).

Guildhall Library
Not contacted but will have large numbers of printed books.

Greater London History Library
40 Northampton Rd., EC1R 0AB.
Printed books.
Barnet Library
Regimental News, the Journal of the Middlesex Regiment 1913–14 (Ref.: 355.31) has some lists of men.
Roll of Service from a local Hendon School. (Ref.: M.S. 11410)
Waltham Forest Library
1. Leyton Library, High Road, Leyton London E10 5QH
Ms Book of Remembrance of former pupils of Leyton Elementary Schools who died 1914–18. Not on open access; phone 0181-539-1223 for information.
2. Waltham Forest Archives and Local History Library, Vestry House Museum, Vestry Road, Walthamstow London E17 9NH. Visits are strictly by appointment; phone 0181-509-1917.
Has a list of men of Leyton Parish in forces 1914. (Ref. L83.1 V5)
Who's Who among the Old Monovians, Sir George Monoux Grammar School, Walthamstow, 1966. Includes list of Old Monovians who died in 1914–18 War. *The Roll of Sacrifice and Roll of Honour, being a Record of Service rendered to King and Country by men of the Parish of Walthamstow in the County of Essex,* Vols. 1–5, G.E. Roebuck. 20,000 names (W.64.1). Held at Waltham Forest Town Hall, Forest Road, Walthamstow, London E17.

CRO
London RO., 40 Northampton Road, EC1R 0AB.
Records of Middx. and London TF Association (contain no lists).
School records.
Parish records may contain Rolls of Service, etc.

Other records
Roll Call of 25th Bn. Middx. Regiment after accident of S.S. Tyndareus, 6th Feb 1917. See *Journal of Orders and Medals Society,* Vol.16, No.4, (Winter 1977), p.222.
Harrow: Memorials of the Great War. (SOG)
Royal Masonic Institution for Boys, Wood Green, London. Roll of Honour. (SOG)
Mill Hill School, Middx. War Record 1914–18. (SOG)
Roll of Service: New Zealand Shipping Co. Ltd., J.B. Westroy and Co., Federal Steam Navigation Co. Ltd., Bint, Potter and Hughes Ltd. (West Middlesex and East of London FHSs)
London County Council Record of War Service 1914–18, printed 1922. 10,164 names of men in LCC employ who served. (Most large London Libraries)
Roll of Honour of Carter Paterson and Co. Ltd., 238 City Road, London. (East of London FHS and IWM)
Davies Lane School Magazine, Oct 1915 (Leytonstone, London) has 7 pages of names of ex-pupils serving.

The *Lady's Field Supplement,* Jan 9th, 1915 gives a list of staff from well-known London shops serving in the forces.
Bermondsey's 'Bit' in the Greatest War, H.F. Morriss, 1919.
Alleyn's School, Dulwich. *Roll of Old Boys Serving in H.M. Forces,* Dulwich, 1915.
Imperial College of Science and Technology. Service List, 1915.
Linton House School, *The Great War, 1914–19.* A Roll of Honour. 1920.
List of the Former Scholars of the Ratcliff Settlement Serving in the War, C.K. Scott, 1917.
Saint Paul's School. *Names of Old Paulines Who Lost their Lives in the War,* 1919.
University of London. *Pro Patria, 1914–16,* 1916.
Inns of Court. *War Book of Gray's Inn Containing Names of Members who Served, with Biographical Notices of Those who Fell,* 1921.
Inner Templers who Volunteered and Served in the Great War. With additional names and correct to December 31, 1923, Chiswick Press, 1921, 24.
Merchant Taylors' School War List and Roll of Honour, 1920.
University of London Officers' Training Corps, Roll of Service, 1914–19, 1921.
Record of those Members of University College, London and of University College Hospital and Medical School who were Killed or who Died on Service, 1914–19, 1922.
University College School. Roll of Honour and War List 1914–18, St. Albans, 1922.
These are the names of the students of St. Bartholomew's Hospital who lost their lives in the Great War. 1926.
The Roll of Honour of the Church of St. Luke's Camberwell, and of the Bradfield Boy's Club. March 1st 1916, London, 1916? With portraits.
The Stock Exchange Memorial of Those who Fell in the Great War MCMXIV–MCMXIX, London, 1920. With portraits.
Temple Church, Templers' Union. *In Memoriam, etc. A Record of Members of the Union Killed During the War of 1914–18,* compiled by A.C. Dixon, London, 1923. With portraits.

NORFOLK

Regiments
The Norfolk Regiment
The Norfolk Yeomanry (The King's Own Royal Regiment)

Books
The History of the Norfolk Regiment 1685–1918, Vols. 1 and 2, Brigadier Loraine Petre, Jarrold & Sons, 1924.
The History of the Yarmouth Battery 1569–1926, Major M.A. Castle, Jarrold & Sons, 1927. (Yeomanry Museum)

Museums
Norfolk Regiment
Shirehall, Market Avenue, Norwich NR1 3JQ.
No lists of men held.
See Yeomanry for 12th Bn.
Norfolk Yeomanry
c/o The Gables, Northwell, Pool Road, Swaffham, Norfolk.
Roll of Norfolk Yeomanry and 12th Bn. (Yeomanry) Norfolk Regiment.
Regimental orders.
See also The Muckleburgh Collection, Weybourne Military Camp, Weybourne, Norfolk NR25 7EGT)
CRO
Norwich
Records of TF Association
List of officers of Norfolk Regiment from 1715.
May be records in parish files. Not checked.
Gately: List of men serving. (PD9/32)
Library
Norfolk Local Studies Library.
Not Checked.

NORTHAMPTONSHIRE

Regiments
The Northamptonshire Regiment
The Northamptonshire Yeomanry

Books
The Northamptonshire Regiment 1914–18, Gale & Polden, 1932.
History of the Northamptonshire Regiment 1742–1934, Lieutenant-Colonel Russell Gurney, Gale & Polden, 1935.
The History of the Northamptonshire and Rutland Militia (3rd Battalion Northants Regiment) 1755–1919, Major C.A. Markham, Reeves & Taylor, 1924.
The Glorious Sixth. A Day-to-Day History of the 6th Battalion Northamptonshire Regiment 1914–18, Peter Jackson, 1975. (CRO)
History of the Raising of the 7th (Service) Battalion Northamptonshire Regiment Guy Paget, Gale & Polden, 1915. (Northants Central Library)
Kitchener's Pioneers, Geoffrey Moore, Geoffrey Moore, 1978. (Northants Central Library)
A Short History of the Northamptonshire Battery, Major T.E.C. Stanley, Peterborough Press, 1926. (Northants Central Library and CRO). Has list of men but believed to be for 1926.

Articles in the *Northampton Independent.*
National Roll of the Great War, Vol. 12. (Central Library)
No known books on Northamptonshire Yeomanry.

Museums
Northamptonshire Regiment
Abington Park Museum, Abington, Northampton NN1 5LW.
No lists of men held.
Northamptonshire Yeomanry
c/o A.E. Saunders, 12 Seaton Road, Uppingham, Rutland.
Scrap books with reports from local papers on annual camps 1902–14. The Secretary
of the Old Comrades Association has a list of a few men from 1914–18.
Nominal Rolls for 'C' Squadron 1/1 Northamptonshire Yeomanry 1914 and 1918.
Some details on 'A' Squadron from diaries and scrap books. Some details of awards
and casualties (nearly all now at CRO).
PRO Kew does not have a complete War Diary.

Hinwick House nr. Rushden
This was a V.A.D. Hospital. The present owner, whose ancestors helped during this
war, still has many group photographs and a leave pass-out book which lists names of
wounded.

CRO
Northants. CRO, Delapre Abbey
Printed books.
*Brave Men who have Gone Forth at the Call of Duty from Woodford (Halse) and
Hinton to the Great European War of 1914. (ZB 345/1).*
Photostat of Northants II Salvation Army. Roll of Honour. (P/8162)
*List of Masters, County Scholars and Staff who Served in HM Forces During the
Great War 1914–19,* NCC Education Committee, 1920. (X 6481)
Raunds, Roll of Honour. (278P/361)
Titchmarsh, List of soldiers to be invited. ZB 73/1/5
There may be other records in parish files.

Library
Northants Central Library
Printed books only.

NORTHUMBERLAND
Regiments
The Northumberland Fusiliers
The King's Own Scottish Borderers (see also Scotland)
The Northumberland Yeomanry (Hussars)
The Yeoman Rifles

Books

The 5th in the Great War. A History of the 1st and 2nd Northumberland Fusiliers 1914–18, Brigadier H.R. Sandilands, G.W. Grigg & Sons, 1938.

When the Lantern of Hope Burned Low. The Story of the 1/4th Northumberland Fusiliers (TF) during the German Offensives of March, April, May 1918, Rev.R.W. Callin, J. Catherall & Co. (not dated).

War History of the 7th Northumberland Fusiliers, Captain F. Buckley, T.M. Grierson, 1920. Nominal Roll on Embarkation. (Museum)

Historical Records of the 9th (Service) Battalion Northumberland Fusiliers, Captain C.H. Cooke, Newcastle and Gateshead Incorporated Chamber of Commerce, 1928. Vol. 1 of a series. Includes Embarkation Roll. (Museum)

Historical Records of the 16th (Service) Battalion, Captain C.H. Cooke, 1923. Vol. 2, Embarkation Roll, Nov 1915. (Museum)

Historical Records of the 18th (Service) Battalion (Pioneers), Lieutenant-Colonel J. Shakespear, 1920. Vol. 3, Embarkation Roll, Jan 1916. (Museum)

Historical Records of the 19th (Service) Battalion (Pioneers), Captain C.H. Cooke, Newcastle and Gateshead Incorporated Chamber of Commerce, 1920. Vol. 4, All who served 1915–18. (Museum)

A Record of the 17th and 32nd Service Battalions Northumberland Fusiliers (NER) Pioneers 1914–19, Lieutenant-Colonel J. Shakepear, Northumberland Press Ltd, 1926.

The Story of the Tyneside Scottish - 20th, 21st, 22nd, 23rd (S) Battalions, by Brigadier-General T. Ternan, Northumberland Press Ltd., 1919.

Irish Heroes in the War. The Tyneside Irish Brigade, T.P. O'Connor and A.J. Keating, Everett & Co. Ltd, 1917. Covers 24th, 25th, 26th, 27th (Service), and 30th (Reserve) Bns. Gives the Enlistment Rolls of the first four. (Museum)

The KOSB in the Great War, Captain Stair Gillon, Thomas Nelson, 1930.

War Record of the 4th Battalion King's Own Scottish Borderers and Lothian Border Horse, by W. Sarley Brown, John McQueen & Son, 1920. (KOSB Museum)

The History of the 7/8 (Service) Battalion of King's Own Scottish Borderers, Captain J. Goss, T.N. Foules, 1920. (KOSB Museum)

History of the Northumberland (Yeomanry) Hussars 1819–1923 by H. Pease. (CRO)

The War History of the 1st Northumbrian Brigade RFA (TF) Aug 1914–July 1919, by Lieutenant-Colonel C.H. Ommanney, J.W. Hindson & Sons, 1927.

The History of the Tyne Electrical Engineers, Royal Engineers 1884–1935, R.W. Ward & Sons Ltd., Newcastle-upon-Tyne, 1935.

Museums

The Northumberland Fusiliers

Fusiliers Museum of Northumberland, The Abbots Tower, Alnwick Castle, Alnwick, Northumberland NE66 1NG.

No records of men held but have many printed books with lists, see above.

Bound volumes of the Regimental Journal, *St. George's Gazette*, contain many names but are not indexed.

The King's Own Scottish Borderers
The Barracks, Berwick-upon-Tweed, Northumberland TD15 1DG.
Printed books and card index of 3,000 welfare cases starting 1920 for widows and men of WW1. Give details of soldier concerned.
Regimental Roll of 1st and 2nd Bns. 1914.
Northumberland Hussars
John George Joicey Museum, City Road, Newcastle-upon-Tyne NE1 2AS.
CRO
Northumberland CRO, N. Gosforth
Printed books.
List of members of 3rd Northumberland Artillery Volunteers 1899–1916. (42) (ZFO).
Yeoman Rifles and enlistment (ZSA 3/107).
TF Association Minutes and A/cs.
Tyne and Wear CRO. Newcastle Archives Department
Accession 48: Papers of Lt. W. Baxter Ellis 1916–17.
Accession 297: Military Service Tribunal Newcastle 1916–18.
Accession 704: Papers J. Douglas 1916.
Accessions 812 and 901: Papers of Capt. A.D. Peacock 1915–18.
Accession 51: Ponteland Cottage Homes Roll of Honour 1914–18.
Also several rolls from firms.
No information given on parish records.
Libraries
Central Library, Newcastle
Not checked.
Newcastle Polytechnic Library
Extensive newspaper cuttings library covering the WWI period. Well indexed.

NOTTINGHAMSHIRE

Regiments
The Sherwood Foresters (Nottinghamshire & Derbyshire Regiment) See Derbyshire
The Nottinhamshire Yeomanry (Sherwood Rangers)
The Nottinghamshire Yeomanry (South Nottinghamshire Hussars)
Books
The Blast of War. A History of Nottingham's Bantams, 15th (S) Battalion, Sherwood Foresters, 1915–19, Maurice Bacon and David Langley, The Sherwood Press Ltd.
The Sherwood Rangers Yeomanry in the Great War 1914–18 Major H. Tallens, Philip Allen & Co. Ltd., 1926.

Historical Records of the South Nottinghamshire Hussars Yeomanry 1794–1924, George Fellows and Benson Freeman, Gale & Polden, 1928. (Museum)

Museums
The Sherwood Foresters
The Castle, Nottingham NG1 6EL.
Sherwood Rangers
The Queen's Own Yeomanry Centre, TA Centre, Cavendish Drive, Carlton, Nottingham NG6 8AQ. By appointment only.
South Nottinghamshire Hussars
TA Centre, Hucknall Lane, Bulwell, Nottingham NG6 8AQ.
No lists of men held other than those given in the book.
CRO
No lists of men held. See Derbyshire.

Library
University Library, University of Nottingham
Many printed books for East Midlands Regiments and parish histories but not searched.
Lists of ex-OTC men who attended annual reunions but only a small fraction of the 1600 total.
Lists of ex-service students at Nottingham University (UR 1404).
Western Union Roll of Honour. List of men connected with congregations and schools of the Western Union of Unitarian and Free Christian Churches. Covers many towns in S.W. England. There is no known list of former University students who served. About 1600 men.
Other records
Nottingham High School in the War 1914–18. (SOG)

OXFORDSHIRE

Regiments
The Oxfordshire and Buckinghamshire Light Infantry (see also Buckinghamshire)
The Oxfordshire Yeomanry (Queen's Own Oxfordshire Hussars)
Books
History of the 43rd and 52nd (Oxfordshire and Buckinghamshire) Light Infantry in the Great War 1914–18, Captain J.E.H. Neville, Aldershot, 1938.
War Record of the 1/4th Battalion Oxford and Bucks Light Infantry, Major P. Pickford, Banbury, Banbury Guardian, 1919. (Oxford Central Library)
The Story of the 2/4th Oxford and Bucks Light Infantry, Captain G.K. Rose, B.H. Blackwell, 1920.

Memorial Record of the 7th (Service) Battalion of the Oxford and Buckinghamshire Light Infantry, Lieutenant-Colonel C. Wheeler, Basil Blackwell, 1921.
The Oxfordshire and Buckinghamshire Light Infantry Chronicle. An annual record 1914–18, Vols. 1–5, The Great War. The Regimental Annual Chronicle.
The Oxfordshire Hussars in the Great War (1914–18), Adrian Keith-Falconer, John Mieway, 1927. (Oxford Central Library)

Museums
The Oxfordshire and Buckinghamshire Light Infantry
TA Centre, Slade Park, Headington, Oxford OX3 7JL and also
The Royal Green Jackets Museum, Peninsular Barracks, Romsey Road, Winchester SO23 8TS.
Queen's Own Oxfordshire Hussars
With Ox. & Bucks. at Headington.
No lists of men held.

CRO
Oxford RO
Printed books (J.E.H. Neville).
List of Oxford C.C. staff killed in WWI is in County Hall, Oxford.

Library
Oxford Central Library
Printed books.
Oxford High School Roll of Service 1914–19.
War record of University Press. Oxford 1923.
Oxford University Roll of Service. (SOG)
Balliol College War Memorial Book 1914–18. (SOG)

Other records
Clanfield Church, Oxon. has a plaque listing all who served.
Old Boys and Masters of Dragon School, Oxford. (SOG)
History of Gt. Staughton, Rev.H.G. Watson, St. Neots, Percy C. Tomson. 1916. Includes 6 pages of all who served.

PETERBOROUGH

See Huntingdonshire.

RUTLAND

See also Leicestershire and Northamptonshire.

Regiments
The 58th Rutlandshire Regiment (2nd Battalion of the Northamptonshire Regiment)
The Leicestershire and Rutland Yeomanry Rifle Volunteers

Books

Rutland and The Great War, G. Phillips. Lists by parish all who served. Edited biographies of the fallen, photographs. Old Oakhamians and Old Uppinghamians, Rutland Volunteer Training Corps, etc.

The History of the Northamptonshire and Rutland Militia (3rd Battalion Northants Regiment) 1755–1919, Major C.A. Markham, Reeves & Taylor, 1924.

Records of POWs, Leicestershire and Rutland. (22D61)

Museums

Rutland County Museum

Catmos Street, Oakham, Rutland LE15 6HW.

See also Northamptonshire Regiment.

SHROPSHIRE

Regiments

The King's Shropshire Light Infantry

The Shropshire Yeomanry

The Shropshire Royal Horse Artillery

Books

The History of the King's Shropshire Light Infantry in the Great War 1914–18, Major W.B. Wood (Ed.), The Medici Society Ltd., 1925. Lists killed and awards. (CRO)

History of the Corps of the King's Shropshire Light Infantry, Vol.IV. (CRO)

The History of the 4th Battalion King's Shropshire Light Infantry (TA) 1745–1945, Lieutenant-Commander P.K. Kemp, Wilding & Son Ltd., 1955. Lists killed 1914–18 and awards.

Historical Records 4th Battalion The King's Shropshire Light Infantry (TA), G. Archer Parfitt, duplicated 1959. (4th Kings Museum)

The Shropshire Militia and Volunteers. List of commanders 1908–59.

The Shropshire Yeomanry, MDCCXCV–MCMXLV (1795–1945). The Story of a Volunteer Cavalry Regiment, E.W. Gladstone, The Whitethorn Press, 1953.

Museum

The Castle, Shrewsbury, Shropshire SY1 2AT. Curator: Mr P. Duckers MA.

Printed books but no other lists.

No research by post but Nominal Rolls of the 1/4, 2/4, 3/4, and 4th Reserve Bn. KSLI may be examined by appointment only. They are arranged by parish, for pre-1914 period only.

CRO

Shrewsbury Records and Research Centre, Castle Gates, Shrewsbury.

Printed books.

Enlistment Rolls (Broseley Detachment 11th Platoon) Shropshire Volunteer Regiment. (SRO 1681/Box 198)
Roll of Honour, Welshampton. (SRO 2608/382, 632)
Roll of Honour, Shropshire killed. (SRO 141/1–2)

Libraries
Shropshire, Castle Gates. Not contacted.

Other records
Shrewsbury School, Roll of Service 1914–18, printed 1921. Gives some 1850 names; indexed.

SOMERSET

Regiments
Prince Albert's (The Somerset Light Infantry)
The North Somerset Yeomanry
The West Somerset Yeomanry

Books
The History of the Somerset Light Infantry (Prince Albert's) 1914–19, Averred Wary, Methuen, 1927.
A History of the 1st Battalion The Somerset Light Infantry (Prince Albert's) July 1st 1916–end of the War, Major V.H.B. Majendie, Goodman, 1921.
The Great War, 1914–19. The Book of Remembrance of the 5th Battalion (Prince Albert's) Somerset Light Infantry, Chiswick Press, 1930.
Scrap book of the 7th Battalion Somerset Infantry (13th Foot). Chronicle of Experience in the Great War 1914–18, Lieutenant-Colonel R.P. Preston-Whyte, 1932 and 1933.
A Record of the West Somerset Yeomanry 1914–18, Captain R.C. Boyle, St. Catherine's Press, 1922.
The History of Somerset Yeomanry, Volunteer and Territorial Units, W.G. Fisher, Goodman & Son, 1924.

Museum
Somerset Military Museum, County Museum, The Castle, Taunton, Somerset TA1 4AA.
Printed books as above plus detailed Roll Book of men in 1st Bn. 1914–19.
War Diaries of some Bns.
There are no known records of the two Yeomanry Regiments.

CRO
  Taunton CRO
List of the inhabitants of Taunton who served in WWI with details of service. (Ref.: D/B/ta/47/7–12)

The Somerset County War Memorial, Phoenix Press, Taunton, 1923. Lists inhabitants of the county who died.

Bath City RO
No lists of men held.

STAFFORDSHIRE

Regiments
The Prince of Wales's (North Staffordshire Regiment)
The South Staffordshire Regiment
The Staffordshire Yeomanry (Queen's Own Royal Regiment)

Books
History of the 1st and 2nd Battalion The North Staffordshire Regiment (The Prince of Wales's) 1914–23, Hughes & Harber Ltd., 1933.

The History of the 7th (Service) Battalion Prince of Wales (North Staffordshire Regiment) 1914–19, L.R. Missen, W. Heffer & Sons, 1920.

History of the 8th North Staffs., Hughes & Harber Ltd., 1921.

A History of the South Staffordshire Regiment 1905–23, James P. Jones, Whitehead Bros., Wolverhampton, 1923.

With the 38th in France and Italy. Being the Record of the Doings of the 1st Battalion South Staffordshire Regiment from 26th Sep 1916–26th May 1918, Lieutenant-Colonel A.B. Beauman, A.C. Lomax's Successors.

The 5th North Staffords and the North Midland Territorials (the 40th and 59th Divs.) 1914–1919, Lieutenant Walter Meakin, Hughes & Harber Ltd., 1920. List of Officers. (Staffordshire CRO)

The Unbreakable Coil, Major A.L.K. Anderson, Whitehead Bros., 1923. Covers 2nd Bn. from Oct 1914 to Dec 1914.

The War History of the Sixth Battalion the South Staffordshire Regiment (TF), Committee of Officers, William Heinemann Ltd., 1924.

The History of the 7th South Staffordshire Regiment, Major A.H. Ashcroft (Ed.), London, 1919.

The Staffordshire Yeomanry (QORR) in the First and Second World Wars 1914–18 and 1939–45, Lieutenant-Commander P.K. Kemp,Gale & Polden Ltd., 1950.

Walsall and District. The Roll of the Great War 1914–18, W.H. Worley. Walsall. Contains approx. 1500 men who served. (Museum Ref. 5210)

Stafford's Roll of Service in the Great War: Aug 4th 1914–June 28th 1919. Contains approx. 3000 who served. (Museum Ref. 5925)

Museums
North and South Staffordshire Regiments
Regimental HQ. Whittington Barracks, Lichfield, Staffs. WS14 9PY.
Nominal Roll 2/5th S. Staffords. Aug 1917. (Ref. 5071)

Roll Book 1st Bn. N. Staffords 1914 some to June 1915. (Ref. 1006)
Roll Book Hospital Admissions 1st Bn. N. Staffords. Sep 1914—Feb 1915. (Ref. 1005).
Roll of all casualties 6th Bn. N. Staffords, 1914—18 war period; 2,000 names. (Ref. 4205)
Wolverhampton press cuttings 1914—18, (Ref. 982).

Staffordshire Yeomanry
The Ancient High House, Greengate Street, Stafford ST16 2HS.
CRO
Lichfield
No lists of men held.
Staffordshire RO
Eastgate St., Stafford.
Printed books on 5th North Staffords.
Staffordshire Yeomanry.
Records of men, Walsall and Burton-on-Trent companies 1913—14, 2 volumes. (Ref. D1300/3/7)

Libraries
WestBromwich
List of men who served from West Bromwich in book in entrance hall.
Wolverhampton Library
Tettenhall Collegiate Church. Those serving from parish.
Walsall Archives
No lists of men held.

Other records
Leek Sailors and Soldiers, Roll of Honour 1914—15, Leek and District, compiled by Leek Sailors and Soldiers Comforts Society, Nov 1915. Printed David Morris Ltd. Lists 1500 names. Gives name, Regiment, where serving, also killed.
The Lichfield Guildhall has a plaque giving the names of all who served with the 'E' (Lichfield) Coy. 6th Bn. The North Staffordshire Regiment.
Ormes School, Wolstanton, Newcastle-under-Lyme. Staffs. (SOG)

SUFFOLK

Regiments
The Suffolk Regiment
The Suffolk Yeomanry (The Duke of York's Own Loyal Suffolk Hussars)
Books
The History of the Suffolk Regiment 1914—18, Lieutenant-Colonel C.C.R. Murphy, Hutchinson, 1928. (CRO)
The Record of the Foreign Service Tour of the 1st Battalion The Suffolk Regiment

1907–27, from the *Digest of Service and the Suffolk Regiment Gazette,* J.S.D. Lloyd, 1926.

The History of the 1/5th Battalion The Suffolk Regiment, Captain A. Fair and Captain E.D. Wolton, Eyre & Spottiswoode Ltd., 1923. (Ipswich CRO)

Museums

SuffolkRegiment

The Keep, Gibraltar Barracks, Out Ribygate Street, Bury St.Edmunds, Suffolk IP33 3RN.

Believed to have some records. Replied but no information given.

Suffolk Yeomanry

The Muckleborough Collection, Weybourne Military Camp, Weybourne, Norfolk NR25 7EG.

No lists of men held.

CRO

Ipswich

Appears to have a good index of records of WWI. This has been published in *Archives News,* Nos. 19 and 20, from the CRO. It includes items from Ipswich and Bury St. Edmunds offices and local studies libraries. Items include:

The 1/5th Suffolk Territorials in the First World War, E.D. Wolton, in *Suffolk Fair,* Aug 1978.

With the 1/5th Suffolks in Gallipoli, E.D. Wolton.

Suffolk Regimental Gazette, for the war years (Jan 1916–Dec 1916).

Illustrated Memorial of the Great War in relation to Leiston and District, J.S. Waddell.

A short record of the East Anglia Munitions Committee in the Great War 1914–18, Sir Wilfred Stokes. (Lowestoft Library)

Booth's Illustrated Almanac 1915–16 lists men from 34 parishes in the Woodbridge district who served.

Marchioness of Bristol's scrapbook. (B:816/5)

Photographs.

National Registration; bundles of forms.

Register of local Tribunals: Leiston-cum-Sizewell.

Appeal Tribunal Minutes: Felixstowe.

Postcards of Hengrave Hospital.

War Memorial papers for Bury St. Edmunds, Ipswich St. Clement and Exning C.P. School.

Many parish records contain lists not listed in Archives News.

Other records

Lowestoft Men, in *Suffolk Roots,* Vol. 9, No. 4, Oct 1983, (Suffolk FHS), gives a list of men.

Parish Church at Butley nr. Woodbridge has two Rolls of Honour dealing with Butley, Capel St. Andrew and Wantisden.

SURREY

Regiments
The Queen's (Royal West Surrey Regiment)
The East Surrey Regiment
The Surrey Yeomanry (Queen Mary's Regiment)

Books
History of the Queen's Royal Regiment, Vol. 7, Colonel H.C. Wylly, Gale & Polden, 1925.
4th The Queen's Royal Regiment. An Unofficial War History, Captain Ronald Bannerman, H.R. Grubb Ltd., 1931. Also covers the 2/5th Bn.
History of the East Surrey Regiment, 3 vols., 1914–17), Colonel H.W. Pearce and Brigadier-General H.S. Slomen, Medici Society, 1933–34.
The History and War Records of the Surrey Yeomanry (Queen Mary's Regiment) 1797–1928, E.D. Harrison-Ainsworth, C. & F. Layton, 1928. Lists killed, awards and officers, also programme of horse races with many names. (CRO).
Several books on London Regiment Bns. who joined the Surrey Regiment (see London). Most are in Lambeth Archives.
Lowfield Heath Remembered, Jean Shelley, The Charlwood Society, 1984. Pages 20 and 21 give a list of all who served from this hamlet in the Parish of Charlwood, Surrey. (Copies in Surrey CRO)
The Soldiers of Caterham 1914–18, Peter Soater, 69 Beechwood Road, Caterham, Surrey. Lists names from many sources.
1914 Letters from a Volunteer, Don Cook (Ed.), D.J.C. Cook, 46 Briarwood Drive, Northwood, Middx. HA6 1PN. Thirty four letters of Sgt. G. Cook while in Dover (E. Surreys).

Museums
The Queens and East Surrey Regiment
Inner Bailey, Dover Castle, Kent CT16 1HU.
No lists of men held.
The Surrey Yeomanry
None located.

CRO
Guildford
List of Officers 6th Surrey Volunteer Regiment. (173/90/4/5)
May be other lists in parish records, e.g. Headley (Hants) has lists for 1915 and 1918. (PSH/HED/22/7–8)

Fig. 4. Another example of a firm's Roll of Honour. This Guildford firm used a common type of preprinted form with the names of all those serving entered by hand. The 'Scrap of Paper' was the treaty of 1831 which guaranteed Belgium's independence.

92

Kingston
Records include 44 recruiting books for Surrey. Covers all Regiments and Corps. 100,000 names.
May be lists in parish records (not in index).
Recruiting Appeal Tribunal. (CC28/303B) Closed for 100 years.
War Relief Committee. (CC7/1/1–5)
War Pensions Committee. (CC7/2/1–4)
War Distress Committee. (CC28/267)
Hersham War Memorial Papers. (2843/9)
Lambeth Archives, Minet Library
Printed books.
War records of the 1st Surrey Rifles 1927.
Awards (no author or publisher given).
Battalion Orders, list of new recruits and extenders of service for 1914. (Ref.: IV/36/1/15)
Officers Record Book. (Ref.: IV/36/5/4)
Roll of Service, Gipsy Road School, Norwood.
Library
Croydon Lending Library
Croydon and the Great War, Moor and Sayess, Corporation of Croydon, 1920. Lists 3,000 dead, awards and prisoners of war.
Other records
Lists of men serving from Carling, Gill and Carling Ltd of Guildford, Surrey Advertiser, June 17th 1983.
Whitgift Book of Remembrance, Whitgift Grammar School Croydon. (SOG)

SUSSEX

Regiments
The Royal Sussex Regiment
The Sussex Yeomanry
Books
An Historical Memoir of the 35th Royal Sussex Regiment of Foot, Richard Trimen, 1873; reprinted 1994.
A History of the Royal Sussex Regiment. A History of the Old Belfort Regiment and the Regiment of Sussex 1703–1953, G.D. Martineau, Moore & Tillyer, 1955.
A Short History of the Royal Sussex Regiment (35th Foot and 107th Foot) 1701–1926.
The History of the Seventh (Service) Battalion of the Royal Sussex Regiment 1914–19, Owen Rutter, The Times Publishing Co., 1934. List of killed only. (W. Sussex CRO)

Account of the Great War of the Various Battalions, Gale & Polden, Aldershot, 1941.
Sussex Yeomanry and the 16th Sussex Yeomanry Battalion Royal Sussex Regiment 1914–19, Lieutenant-Colonel H.I. Powell-Edwards, Andrew Melrose Ltd., 1921. Lists of all who served. (W. Sussex CRO)

Museum
The Sussex Combined Services Museum, Redoubt Fortress, Royal Parade, Eastbourne, Sussex BN22 7AQ.
This covers all Sussex units.

CROs
Chichester
All records of the Royal Sussex Regiment are at the CRO, Chichester including:
2nd Bn. Nominal Roll, 1914–19. (RSR Ms. 2/65)
4th Bn. Nominal Roll Suvla Bay, 8 Aug 1915. (RSR Ms 4/72)
4th Bn. Nominal Roll, 1918. (RMS Ms 4/87)
5th (Cinque Ports) Bn. Nominal Roll, 1915–17. (RSR Ms 5/82)
5th (Cinque Ports) Bn. Nominal Roll, 1915–18. (RSR Ms 5/83)
5th (Cinque Ports), 1918. (RMS Ms 6/8)
2/6th Bn. Nominal Roll, printed in the *Royal Sussex Herald* (The Bn. Journal), Sep 1916. (RMS Ms 6/8)
Several Rolls for pre-war Bns. 1898–1914.
Bn. orders for 2nd, 4th, 5th and 2/6th Bns. for some periods during the war.
List of all casualties for 5th (Cinque Ports) Bn. (RSR Ms 5/72)
The total collection of records in the CRO amounts to 80 boxes, 25 feet of printed books and 7,000 photographs.
A detailed catalogue of the collection entitled *Records of the Royal Sussex Regiment* by A.E.Readmann, published 1986 by West Sussex County Council, has some 250 pages.
A check of the parish catalogues has located Rolls of Honour (or Service) and/or War Memorial Committee minutes from the following parishes: West Dean, Fernhurst Balcombe, Cuckfield, Angmering, Worth, New Shoreham, Crawley, Wisborough Green, Slinfold, Clayton, Cowfold, Chichester (St. Paul).

East Sussex CRO
The Maltings, The Castle Precinct, Lewes.
The CRO reports that both the *East Sussex News* and the *East Grinstead Observer* published full lists of volunteers from 1914. Brighton and Eastbourne were excluded.
TF Minute Books.
Newick Boys School WWI Roll of Honour. (AMs 5785/8)

Other records
Eastbourne College Roll of War Service 1914–18. (SOG)
Members of London, Brighton and South Coast Railway on active service 1914–18 Public Record Office, Kew, (RAIL 414/761).

WARWICKSHIRE

Regiments
The Royal Warwickshire Regiment
The Warwickshire Yeomanry

Books
The Story of the Royal Warwickshire Regiment (formerly the Sixth Foot), Charles Lethbridge Kingsford, Country Life Ltd., London, 1921. (RWR Museum)
The 11th Royal Warwicks in France 1915–16, Brevet-Colonel C.S. Collison, Cornish Brothers Ltd., 1928. (Warwick RO)
The War Record of the 1/5th Battalion The Royal Warwickshire Regiment, Lieutenant C.E. Carrington, Cornish Bros. Ltd., 1922. (Birmingham Reference Library)
History of the 1/6th Battalion of the Royal Warwickshire Regiment, Cornish Bros. Ltd., Birmingham, 1922. (Birmingham Reference Library)
History of the 2/6th Battalion The Royal Warwickshire Regiment 1914–19, Cornish Bros.Ltd., Birmingham, 1929. (Birmingham Reference Library)
Black Square Memories. An Account of the 2/8th Battalion The Royal Warwickshire Regiment 1914–18, H.T. Chidgey, Shakespeare Head Press, 1924. Lists officers only.
The First Birmingham Battalion in the Great War 1914–19. Being a History of the 14th (Service) Battalion of the Royal Warwickshire Regiment, J.E.B. Fairclough, Cornish Brothers Ltd., 1933. (Birmingham Reference Library)
The 15th Battalion Royal Warwickshire Regiment (2nd Birmingham Battalion) in the Great War, Major C.A. Bill, Cornish Brothers Ltd., 1932. (RWR Museum)
Birmingham City Battalion Book of Honour, Sir William H. Bowater, Sherratt and Hughes, 1919. (Birmingham Reference Library)
Birmingham Pals. The story of the 14th, 15th and 16th Battalions of the Royal Warwickshire Regiment, Terry Carter. A history of the three Birmingham City Battalions in World War I.
By God They can Fight, Peter Caddick-Adams. The story of 143 Infantry Brigade 1908–55.
The Warwickshire Yeomanry in the Great War, Hon. H.A. Adderley, W.H.Smith & Son, 1922. (Birmingham Reference Library)
The Birmingham Territorial Units of the Royal Army Medical Corps 1914–19, Lieutenant-Colonel J.E.H. Sawyer, Allday Ltd., 1921. (Birmingham Reference Library)

Museums
Royal Warwickshire Regiment
St. Johns House, Warwick CV34 4NF.
Printed books.

95

Lists of men who served in Birmingham 14th, 15th and 16th (Service) Bns. RWR (printed books) give pre-war places of employment.
Birmingham City Battalions Book of Honour.
Warwickshire Yeomanry
The Court House, Jury Street, Warwick CV34 4EW.
CRO
Warwick
1913 Roll of Warwickshire Yeomanry.
1914 Roll of 'B' sqn. Warwickshire Yeomanry. List of those who served in Ratley.
Coventry
Printed books.
Supplement to *Coventry Herald* Christmas 1914. List of men from Coventry Kenilworth, Bedworth and District.
Our Part in the World War 1914–18, List of British Thomson-Houston Co. employees
List of King Edward's School, Birmingham, ex pupils who served.
Libraries
Dudley Local History Library
Printed books only.
Birmingham Reference Library
Bournville Works and the War. A Record of the Firm's Workers' Activities 1914–19 Messrs. Cadbury Bros. Ltd. Lists of all who went to war. (Accession No. 28615(F/2)
Birmingham Public Libraries Staff in WWI. Record of the War Service of Member of the staff 1914–18.
Birmingham City Bns. Book of Honour. *Rolls of Honour of Men from City Firm, and Institutions,* Sir William H. Bowater (Ed.), Sherratt & Hughes, 1919.
List of Old Edwardians Serving in His Majesty's Forces, R.C. Gilson. (Acc. N(270484 L 48.111)
The Oratory School and the War. A Roll of Honour, 1916, (Acc. No. 321503 LP 17.121'
Other records
The Warwick Advertiser had many lists in the issues published during the war These include volunteers by school and village, casualties, POWs, awards, et(Confined to villages around Warwick.
Rugby School War Register. (SOG)

WESTMORLAND

See Cumbria.

WILTSHIRE

Regiments
The Duke of Edinburgh's (Wiltshire Regiment)
The Royal Wiltshire Yeomanry (Prince of Wales's Own Royal Regiment)

Books
The Story of the Wiltshire Regiment (Duke of Edinburgh's), the 62nd and 99th Foot (1756–1959), Colonel N.C.E. Kenrick, Gale & Polden Ltd., 1963.
The 2nd Battalion Wiltshire Regiment (99th). A Record of their Fighting in the Great War 1914–18, Major W.S. Shepherd, Gale & Polden Ltd., 1927.
The 1/4th Battalion The Wiltshire Regiment 1914–19, Lieutenant George Blick, Butler & Tanner Ltd., 1923.

Museums
The Duke of Edinburgh's (Wiltshire Regiment)
Redcoats in The Wardrobe, 58 The Close, Salisbury, Wiltshire SP1 2EX.
Has no records of men.
The Royal Wiltshire Yeomanry
Thamesdown Museum, Swindon.
Has very few records and no printed books.
RWY 'B' sqn. Roll Book 4 Aug 1914–March 1917.
'A' sqn. Roll Book 1915–June 1916.
'B' sqn. Roll Book May 1916–April 1918.
The TA Drill Hall
Church Place, Swindon.
May have some records; not contacted.

CRO
Trowbridge.

Other records
War Records of Corsham 1914–19, printed by W.H. Smith & Sons at the Arden Press, London SE1. Lists 719 who served, 115 killed, 24 POWs, plus VADs and Red Cross.

WORCESTERSHIRE

Regiments
The Worcestershire Regiment
The Worcestershire Yeomanry (The Queen's Own Worcestershire Hussars)
The Worcestershire Artillery (67th (Worcestershire) Field Regiment)

Books
N *The Worcestershire Regiment in the Great War*, Captain H. Fitzm. Stacke, G.T. Cheshire & Sons Ltd., 1929. List of awards. (Museum)
1/8th Battalion The Worcestershire Regiment 1914–18, Lieutenant-Colonel H.T. Clarke and Colonel W.K. Peake, War Narratives Publishing Co., 1919.

The Worcestershire Regiment. War Story of the 1/8th (Territorial) Battalion, E.C. Corbett, Herald Office, 1921.
The Yeomanry Cavalry of Worcestershire, 1914–22, Vols. 1 and 2, by 'C' (Viscount Cobham), Vol. 3, by W. Guttery. Mark & Moody. (Museum and St. Helen's Library)
267. *A Short History of the Worcestershire Artillery 1864–1964,* I.S. Swinnerton, Mark & Moody Ltd, Stourbridge, 1964.

Museums
  The Worcestershire Regiment
Norton Barracks, Worcester WR5 2PA.
Records of Service, Officers.
Records of Service, Soldiers. A few only.
Embarkation Rolls for France for some battalions.
Some citations for decorations and awards.
Personal papers and diaries.
Photographs.
Regimental Magazines from 1922. Contain some obituaries of men who served in WWI.
Soldiers Died in the Great War, Worcestershire.
  The Worcestershire Yeomanry
Worcester City Museum, Foregate St., Worcester WR1 1DT.
Nominal Roll 1914–18.
Printed books.
Two volumes of a Casualty Register. (Ref. Y169)

CRO
  Worcester
TF Minute Books, etc. (Ref. BA5204)
Papers of J.S. Preece, which include a casualty list. (Ref. BA 5334)

Library
  County Library, Worcester
Printed books.
  Worcester City Library
Newspapers.

Other records
Draft of official history of Worcestershire TF Association is in Cheshire CRO. (Ref. Acc.2332/5)

YORKSHIRE

Because of the number of Regiments involved, the regiments covering the whole county will be dealt with first and then the regiments specifically affiliated to each of the three Ridings.

County regiments
The King's Own (Yorkshire Light Infantry)
Alexandra, Princess of Wales's Own (Yorkshire Regiment), popularly known as The
Green Howards
The York and Lancaster Regiment
The Yorkshire Dragoons (Queen's Own)
The Yorkshire Hussars Yeomanry (Alexandra, Princess of Wales's Own)

Books
History of the King's Own Yorkshire Light Infantry in the Great War, Lieutenant-
Colonel R.C. Bond; Vols. 1 and 2, Colonel H.C. Wylly, Vol. 3, Percy Lund,
Humphries & Co. Ltd, 1930.
*A Brief History of the 12th Battalion King's Own Yorkshire Light Infantry
(Pioneers). The Miners Battalion,* Captain R. Ede England, John Lindley, no date.
The History of the Green Howards. 300 Years of Service, Geoffrey Powell, Arms &
Armour Press, 1992.
The Green Howards in the Great War 1914–19, Colonel H.C. Wylly, Butler & Tanner
Ltd, 1926. (Joint Services Collection Wakefield)
*The Green Howards (Alexandra, Princess of Wales Own Yorkshire Regiment). For
Valour 1914–18,* Richmond, York. No date or publisher.
The History of the 7th Service Battalion, the Green Howards, Colonel R.d'A Fife,
c.1920
The York and Lancaster Regiment 1758–1919, Vols. 1 and 2, Colonel H.C. Wylly,
Butler & Tanner Ltd., 1930.
The 1/4th (Hallamshire) Battalion York and Lancaster Regiment 1914–19, Captain
D.P. Grant, The Arden Press, 1931. (Rotherham Central Library)
A Short History of the 2nd Volunteer Battalion York and Lancaster Regiment,
Norman Anton, Express Office. (Rotherham Central Library)
*History of the 7th Service Battalion The York and Lancaster Regiment (Pioneers)
1914–19,* Captain M.T. Gilvary, The Talbot Press Ltd., 1921. Lists killed and
wounded. (Sheffield City Library)
A History of the 9th (Service) Battalion The York and Lancaster Regiment 1914–19,
J.B. Montagu, duplicated 1934.
History of the 12th Service Battalion York and Lancaster Regiment, R.A. Sparling,
J.W. Northend Ltd., 1920. (Wakefield District Library)
A Short Record of the Queen's Own Yorkshire Dragoons 1794–1930, Colonel C.J.
Hurst and Major R. Warde-Aldam (Eds.), Doncaster, 1931.

Museums
King's Own Yorkshire Light Infantry
Chequer Road, Doncaster DN1 2AE
Holds copies of War Diaries, printed books and list of all men killed.

The Green Howards
Trinity Church Sq., Richmond DL10 4QN.
Holds list of all men killed, wounded and missing and POW.
York and Lancaster Regiment
Rotherham Libraries, Museum and Arts Department.
Has list of Regimental casualties.
The Yorkshire Hussars and The Queen's Own Yorkshire Dragoons
The Yorkshire Yeomanry Museum, Yeomanry Barracks, Fulford Road, York YO1 4ES.
CRO
None of the Yorkshire ROs or Libraries listed in the Record Office Report contacted had any Military records.
Civil records are covered in the Ridings.

YORKSHIRE (EAST RIDING)

Regiments
The East Yorkshire Regiment
The East Riding of Yorkshire Yeomanry

Books
The East Yorkshire Regiment in the Great War 1914–18, E. Wyrall, Harrison, 1928.
Record of Service of the 4th (Hull) and 13th (S) Battalions of the East Yorkshire Regiment, Townley Truman, R. Johnson & Sons, no date.
The History of the 10th Service Battalion of the East Yorkshire Regiment (Hull Commercials) 1914–18, A. Brown, London, 1937. (4th Bn. Museum)
Some of Them. A short Diary of the 11th (S) Battalion of the East Yorkshire Regiment 1914–19, Goddard, Walker & Brown, Hull, 1921.
Records of the East Yorkshire Volunteer Force (1914–19), Colonel W. Lambert White and Major F.H. Lock (Eds.), Eastern Morning and Hull News Co. Ltd., 1920. (4th Bn. Museum)
Destiny. The War Letters of Captain Jack Oughtred MC 1915–18 Alan Wilkinson (Ed.), Clifford Ward & Co. (Bridlington) Ltd., 1996.
Grandfather's Adventures in the Great War 1914–18, Cecil M. Slack, Arthur H. Stockwell Ltd., Devon, 1977.

Museums
The East Yorkshire Regiment
The Prince of Wales's Own Regiment of Yorkshire Museum, 3 Tower Street, York YO1 1SB.
Artefacts and records of the former East Yorkshire Regiment.
No lists of soldiers or personal records held.

4th Bn. East Yorkshire Regiment
Hull City Museums, Wilberforce House, High Street, Hull.
No display but collection may be viewed by appointment (Tel. 01482–593293).
'D' Coy Roll Roll Book 13–16 Platoons.
1/4 East Yorks 1914. (Ref.: 25.72.194)
'D' Coy Roll Book 1/4 Bn. East Yorks 1914. (Ref.: 25.72.178)
7th Hull Bn. Scrapbook with photographs. (Ref.: 25.72.318)
Printed books.
CRO
Grimsby
Roll of Honour for Scunthorpe Urban District. All who served. (SHARO 518/5/3)
Inspection Records of Wintringham School OTC Grimsby 1908–64 may include boys
   who served. (Ref. 233)
Hull City RO. Kingston upon Hull
List of employees of Humber Conservancy who served in the war. (Ref.
   DPD/1/11/1–3).
Humberside CRO, Beverley
List of old scholars of Spring Bank Orphanage, Hull who served up to 30th June 1915.
   (PE 2/6)
East Yorks TF Minute Books, etc.

Other records
Sledmere Church has a list of men in the Hundred who served; 100 page book.
Middleton on the Wold. Plaque in the church gives all who served.

YORKSHIRE (WEST RIDING)

Regiments
The Prince of Wales' Own (West Yorkshire Regiment)
The Duke of Wellington's (West Riding Regiment)
Books
The West Yorkshire Regiment in the War 1914–18, Vols. 1 and 2, Everard Wyrall,
   John Lane, The Bodley Head Ltd., 1924–27. (Central Library Halifax)
History of the Sixth Battalion, West Yorkshire Regiment, Vol. 1, 1/6th Bn., Captain
   E.V. Tempest. List of Officers. (Central Library Rotherham)
History of the Sixth Battalion, West Yorkshire Regiment, Vol. 2, 2/6th Bn. Captain,
   E.C. Gregory, Percy Lund, Humphries & Co. Ltd., Bradford, 1921–23. Lists
   Officers, senior NCOs and awards. (Doncaster Central Library)
*History of the Prince of Wales Own West Yorkshire Regiment 11th (Service)
   Battalion,* Major C.L. Armstrong, J.D. Todd, 1919.
The Bradford Pals, R.N. Hudson. (16th and 18th POW West Yorks. Regiment).
Leeds Pals 1914–1918, Laurie Milner, Leo Cooper, London 1991.

Leeds at War, J.M. Hagerty, E.P. Publishing Ltd., Wakefield.
History of the Duke of Wellington's West Riding Regiment During the First Three Years of the Great War from Aug 1914–Dec 1917, J.J. Fisher, G.T. Witehead, printers. List of wounded and POWs. (Central Library, Halifax)
History of the Duke of Wellington's Regiment (1st and 2nd Battalions) 1881–1923, Brigadier-General C.D. Bruce, Medici Society, 1927. (Central Library Halifax)
The History of the 1/4th Battalion Duke of Wellington's (West Riding) Regiment 1914–19, Captain P.G. Bales, Edw. Mortimer Ltd., 1920.
The West Riding Territorials in the Great War, Laurie Magnus, Kegan Paul, French, Trubner & Co. Ltd., 1920. List of awards. (Central Library Halifax)

Museums
   The Prince of Wales's Own Regiment of Yorkshire Museum
3 Tower St., York YO1 1SB.
Artefacts and records of the former West Yorkshire Regiment.
No lists of men held or their personal records.
   The Duke of Wellington's Regimental Museum
Bankfield Museum, Akroyd Park, Halifax HX3 6HG.
Embarkation List for 2nd Bn.
Personal diaries.
Photographs.
Printed books.
   Bradford Pals Museum (16th and 18th POW West Yorks)
Bradford Art Galleries and Museums.
Some items relating to the Bradford Pals but no records.

CRO
   West Yorks RO, Calderdale
Sowerby Bridge War Pensions Minute Book. (Ref. SPL. 292)
List of men from Midgley who served. (NOR: 51/1–8)
   West Yorks RO, Leeds
There may be lists in parish files.
   West Yorks RO, Wakefield
Bradford Grammar School collection includes lists. (C 369/143, 144)
   West Yorks RO, Bradford
Not checked.
   West Yorks RO, Huddersfield
Not checked.

Libraries
   Wakefield Archives Dept. Library HQ
Printed books only.

Rotherham, Brian O'Malley Central Library
Printed books only, in Local Studies Library.
Brotherton Library, University of Leeds
The Liddle Archive: large collection of War Diaries.
Kirklees Central Library
District Archives: no records.
Local History Library: printed books only.
Calderdale Central Library. Halifax
Printed books only.
Doncaster Central Library. Archive Department
Printed books.
Records of Trinity Presbyterian Church, Doncaster.
Files of *Doncaster Gazette* and *Doncaster Chronicle*.
Doncaster Central Library. Local History Library
Not checked.
Sheffield City Library.
Printed books.
List of men from Wombwell Main Colliery near Barnsley who enlisted. (NCB 982).
Sheffield City Museum, Weston Park
Not contacted but may have memorial plaques from defunct local firms.
Sheffield University Library
Sheffield University Annual Reports 1914/15–1918/19 list casualties, etc. and roll of service.
Leeds Museum
Some material on Leeds Rifles but no lists.
Leeds City Library
Not contacted but has a set of Absent Voters' Lists for Leeds.
York City Archives. Exhibition Sq.
List of all men from York serving in forces; with manuscript index (initial letter only), also list of POWs. (Town clerk's parcel 1378/1)
Electoral Rolls for 1914, 1915, 1918, 1919 which give names only of men in Quarters at local barracks. Also 1918 and 1919 Absent Voters' List.
The King's Book of York Fallen Heroes is in St.Martin's Church, Coney Street, York. It lists 1443 individuals with photographs of all but 19.

All these sources have been indexed by Ken Haywood of the City of York FHS, and this can be seen at York City Archives.

Other records
Craven's Part in the Great War, John T. Clayton (Ed.). Lists all serving men.
Burn Cross, Bracken Hill and Charlton Brook Patriotic Club published a booklet which gives accounts. Names of 18 men killed and 117 who 'responded to the call'. No date, but the club was formed Nov 1915.

Ravensthorpe Parish Church has many photographs. Contact Rev. I. Wildey, St. Saviours Vicarage, Church St., Ravensthorpe, Dewsbury. WF13 3LA.

YORKSHIRE (NORTH RIDING)

Regiment
There is no specific North Riding Regiment.

Books
A Brief History of the Territorial Force Association of the County of York (North Riding) 1908–19, Captain F.H. Reynard, Jos. Walker, 1919.
The North Riding of Yorkshire Volunteers 1914–19, Colonel Sir James D. Legard, The Yorkshire Herald Co., 1919.

Museum
Although not a specific North Riding regiment, the museum of the Green Howards is at Trinity Church Square, Richmond, N. Yorks DL10 4QN.

CRO
Cleveland CRO Middlesborough
List of Middlesborough men awarded decorations.
Roll of Honour, St. Albans Church, Middlesborough. (PR/M(AD)6/1)

Libraries
Borthwick Institute of Historical Research, York
Roll of Service for York St. Maurice. (PR Y/MAUR 22)
List of men of Holme on Spalding Moor. (PR H/SM 60)
List of men for Norton. (PR NORT 72)
Middlesborough Central
Not contacted.

11

WELSH REGIMENTS

THE WELSH REGIMENTS

The Welsh Guards (see under Guards)
The Royal Welch Fusiliers
The South Wales Borderers
The Welch Regiment
The Monmouthshire Regiment
The Denbighshire Yeomanry
The Glamorgan Yeomanry
The Montgomeryshire Yeomanry
The Pembroke Yeomanry
The Flintshire Yeomanry
The Welsh Horse Yeomanry
The Royal Monmouthshire Royal Engineers

THE ROYAL WELCH FUSILIERS

Books
Regimental Records of the Royal Welch Fusiliers, Vol. III, France and Flanders
 1914–18, Vol.IV, Turkey, Bulgaria and Austria 1915–18, C.H. Dudley Ward, Forster,
 Groom & Co. Ltd., 1929. Reprinted 1995.
That Astonishing Infantry. Three Hundred Years of the History of the Royal Welch
 Fusiliers (23rd Regiment of Foot), 1689–1989, M. Glover, London, 1989.
The Story of the Royal Welch Fusiliers, H. Tipping, London, 1915.
The War the Infantry Knew 1914–18. The 2nd Battalion in the Great War, Dr J.C.
 Dunn, King & Sons, London, 1938. Reprinted by Janes 1987.
The 4th (Denbighshire) Battalion Royal Welsh Fusiliers in the Great War, Wrexham,
 1926.
A Brief Record of the Activities of the 7th Battalion The Royal Welch Fusiliers
 1908–46, Llanidloes, 1950.
The War Diary (1914–18) of the 10th (Service) Battalion Royal Welch Fusiliers,
 Plymouth, 1926.
14th (Service) Battalion, Royal Welch Fusiliers War Diary 1914–19, Aldershot, 1920.

105

Witness these Letters, C.D. Roberts, Gee & Sons (Denbigh) Ltd., 1983.
Ar Orwell Pell, E. Benyon Davies, Llandysull, 1965.

Museum

Queens Tower, Caernarfon Castle, Caernarfon, Gwynedd LL55 2AY.
Unique collection of medals, uniforms, firearms, silver, portraits, etc.
Archive containing extensive collection of photographs and documents including complete set of WWI War Diaries.
Viewing by appointment only (Tel: 01286-673362)

CRO

Gwynedd Archive Service
Caernarfon Area RO
Diary of Sgt. S.F. Williams, Royal Welch Fusiliers. (XM/30/6,7)
TF Association Records of Anglesey, Caernarfonshire, Merioneth and Montgomery.
List of recruits: Moriah Chapel Caernarfon 1914–18. (X/Moriah/62–64,66)
Papers of Caernarfon Motor Battalion Volunteer Regiment. (X/Vaynol/3688–3737)

Anglesey

No records.

Dolgellau

No records.

THE SOUTH WALES BORDERERS

Books

History of the South Wales Borderers, 1914–18, C.T. Atkinson, Medici Society. Roll of Honour and Awards.

Museum

The museum holds some War Diaries, personal diaries and field messages.

THE WELCH REGIMENT

Books

The History of the Welch Regiment, A.C. Whitehorne and T.O. Marden, Western Mail and Echo, Cardiff, 1932. Covers the services of the regiment in the Great War of 1914–18. Lists awards and NCOs.

The 6th Welsh in France 1914–19, RGVM Bland, Western Mail Ltd., Cardiff, 1920.

Museum

The Welch Regiment Museum (41st/69th Foot) (RRW)
The Black and Barbican Towers, Cardiff Castle, Cardiff CF1 2RB.
The regimental records include copies of the War Diaries of every combatant WWI Bn. (the originals are in the PRO), Rolls of Honour, Field Notebooks which list wounded, personal diaries and reminiscences, records of officers' services and

information on POWs (1914—15 only). The only personal records of service held are personal copies of original documents deposited by ex-members of the regiment or their next of kin.
4th Bn. Muster Roll 1914.
6th Bn. Nominal Roll of men proceeding to France; other part Nominal Rolls.
   The Curator invites enquiries from next of kin or the public at large who include a stamped, addressed envelope or 3 International Reply Coupons. He is aware of an expert who has made extensive studies of men of the Regiment.
CRO
   Glamorgan RO
Reports that Glamorgan area TF records were destroyed.
Cowbridge Grammar School records. Roll of Service (Ref.: D/D Cow 19). Roll of
   Service Magazines. (Ref.: D/D Cow 27)
History of Lewis School, Pengam, Arthur Wright, 1929. Lists old boys killed and
   awards (Lib. 2/6).
Local newspapers.
South Glamorgan Ref. Library, Cardiff also has local newspapers.

THE MONMOUTHSHIRE REGIMENT

Books
On the Western Front. 1/3rd Bn. Monmouthshire Regiment 1914—18, Seargeant Bros.
   Ltd., Abergavenny, 1926. Roll of Honour and Awards.
History of the 2nd Battalion Monmouthshire Regiment, Captain G.A. Brett, Hughes
   & Sons, 1933. Roll of Honour and Awards.
Story of the Monmouthshire Volunteer Artillery, Captain J. More and Colonel
   W.L.C. Phillips, Hughes & Sons, 1958. Officers only.
Museum
The Barracks, Brecon, Powys LD3 7EB.
CRO
   Gwent. Cwmbran
Old Monmouthians in forces. (Ref. D262—21)
Church Scout Patrol Book, Panteg with fate in war.
Roll of Honour Abersychan, Newport, Griffithstown. List of servicemen.
TF Newspapers, cuttings 1st Bn. Monmouthshire Regiment.
Record of Service (1914—18 officers).
8th Div. Monmouthshire National Reserve, members and Nominal Roll.

THE DENBIGHSHIRE HUSSARS

Books
None known.

Museum
None known.

CRO

Clwyd RO, Hawarden, Deeside
List of officers (Ref.: TA/FD/17).
TF Minute Book (TA/D/6).
Denbighshire and Flintshire TF Minute Books.
Record Cards of Flintshire men who served. (Ref.: D/DM/181)
Denbighshire Yeomanry, officers. (TA/FD/17)
Mold Parish Roll of Honour. (P/45/1/380)
Police VCs. (D/DM/646/7)

Ruthin, Clwyd
Local Newspapers.
Old Boys of Grove Park Grammar School, Wrexham, Old Boys of Grove Park
    Grammar School, Oswestry who served in the Royal Welch Fusiliers. (DD/GL/192)
Grove Park School, Wrexham, book of photographs. (D/GS/11/84)

THE GLAMORGAN YEOMANRY

Books
Glamorgan. Its Gentlemen Yeomanry, Bryn Owen, Starling Press, 1983.

Museum
The War Diary of 24th Battalion of The Welch Regiment, the battalion formed from
the dismounted Welsh Yeomanry regiments which included the Glamorgan
Yeomanry, is held at the Museum of the Welch Regiment at Cardiff.

THE MONTGOMERYSHIRE YEOMANRY

Books
The Historical Records of the Montgomeryshire Yeomanry, 1909–19, Vol. 2, Colonel
    R.W. Williams Wyn and Major W.N. Stable, Woodall, Minshall, Thomas & Co.
    Ltd., Oswestry 1926.

Museum
Powysland Museum and Montgomery Canal Centre (Montgomeryshire Yeomanry
    Cavalry), The Canal Wharf, Welshpool, Powys SY21 7AQ.
Includes a section on the Montgomeryshire Yeomanry Cavalry.

CRO

Gwynedd Archive Service, Caernarfon Area RO
TF Minute Book and A/cs. Gwent, Cwmbran, ditto.

THE PEMBROKE YEOMANRY

Books
History of the Pembroke Yeomanry (1794–1959), with a Foreword by Major-General L.H.A. Pugh, Haverfordwest, TA Centre, 1959.

Museum
The Pembroke Yeomanry Trust, Castle Museum & Art Gallery, The Castle, Haverfordwest, Dyfed SA61 2EF.

Museum
The War Diary of 24th Battalion of The Welch Regiment, the battalion formed from the dismounted Welsh Yeomanry Regiments which included the Pembroke Yeomanry, is held at the Museum of the Welch Regiment at Cardiff.

THE WELSH HORSE YEOMANRY

Book
Owen Roscomyl and the Welsh Horse, Bryn Owen, Palace Books, Caernarfon 1990.

Museum
None known.

General Information

Books
History of the 38th Welsh Division, Lieutenant-Colonel J.E. Munby, London, 1920.

National Library of Wales
Printed books.
Roll books 'D' Coy 20th Bn. and 'E' Coy 16th Bn. Royal Welch Fusiliers. (NLP 6079 – 6080A)
List of men from Llansilin, Denbigh. (NLW4556E)

CROs
All the Welsh CROs were contacted.

Dyfed-Ceredigion RO., Aberystwyth
Local newspapers.
No other records.

Dyfed: Carmarthen RO and Haverfordwest RO
Former pupils of Queen Elizabeth Grammar School, Carmarthen. Carmarthen RO Ed.(Bk/576/61).

12

SCOTTISH REGIMENTS

As most Scottish Regiments have names that do not connect the Regiment with one particular county, all Regiments are grouped together and the whole country treated as one large 'county'.

THE SCOTTISH REGIMENTS

The Scots Guards (see Guards)
The Royal Scots (Lothian Regiment)
The Royal Scots Fusiliers
The King's Own Scottish Borderers
The Cameronians (Scottish Rifles)
The Black Watch (Royal Highlanders)
The Highland Light Infantry
The Seaforth Highlanders (Rosshire, Buffs,
    The Duke of Albany's)
The Gordon Highlanders
The Queen's Own (Cameron) Highlanders
Princess Louise's (Argyll and Sutherland) Highlanders

For the following, see the Cavalry section.

2nd Dragoons (Royal Scots Greys)
The Ayrshire Yeomanry (Earl of Carrick's Own)
The Fife and Forfar Yeomanry (see Black Watch)
The Queen's Own Royal Glasgow Yeomanry
The Lanarkshire Yeomanry
The Lothians and Border Horse Yeomanry
1st Lovat's Scouts Yeomanry
2nd Lovat's Scouts Yeomanry
The Scottish Horse (see Black Watch)

Books
The Royal Scots 1914–19, Vols. 1 and 2, Major John Ewing, Oliver & Boyd, 1925.
With the Incomparable 29th (5th Battalion The Royal Scots,) Major A.H. Mure, W.&
R. Chambers Ltd., 1919.
The History of the Royal Scots Fusiliers, 1678–1918, John Buchan, Nelson, 1925.
The KOSB in the Great War, Captain Stair Gillon, Thomas Nelson, 1930.
*War Record of the 4th Battalion King's Own Scottish Borderers and Lothian and
Border Horse,* W. Sorley Brown (Ed.), John McQueen & Sons 1920.
War History of the 5th Battalion King's Own Scottish Borderers, G.F. Scott Elliot,
Robert Dinwiddie, 1928.
The History of the 7/8th (Service) Battalion of the King's Own Scottish Borderers,
Captain J. Goss, T.N. Foulis, 1920.
The History of the Cameronians (Scottish Rifles), Vol. 2, 1910–33, Colonel H.H.
Story, Hazell, Watson & Viney, 1961.
*Regimental Roll of Honour of Officers, WOs, NCOs and men of the Cameronians
(Scottish Rifles) 1914–18,* Gale & Polden, Aldershot.
The Fifth Battalion The Cameronians (Scottish Rifles) 1914–19, D. Martin, Jackson
Son & Co., 1936. Roll of men who landed in France 5th Nov 1914. (Glasgow,
Mitchell Library).
With the 8th Scottish Rifles 1914–19, Colonel J.M. Findlay, Blackie & Son Ltd., 1926.
*The 10th Battalion The Cameronians (Scottish Rifles). A Record and a Memorial
1914–18,* The Edinburgh Press, 1923.
*The Black Watch (The Royal Highland Regiment). With the Highland Regiment in
Mesopotamia 1916–17,* Captain H.J. Blampied, The Times Press, 1918. (By an
Officer of the Regiment.)
History of the Black Watch (Royal Highlanders) in the Great War 1914–18, Vol. 3,
A.G. Wauchope (Ed.), Medici Society, London, 1925. List of officers, casualties,
awards. (Dundee Central Library)
The Regular, Militia, Volunteer TA and Service Battalions HLI 1882–1918, Vol. 3,
Lieutenant-Colonel L.B. Oatts, House of Grant Ltd., 1961. (A 4 volume set.)
The 2nd Battalion Highland Light Infantry in the Great War, Major A.D. Telfer-
Smollett, Major C.J. Wallace and Captain H. Ross Skinner, John Horn Ltd., 1929.
The Fifth Battalion Highland Light Infantry in the War 1914–18, Maclehose,
Jackson & Co., Glasgow, 1921.
*An Epic of Glasgow. History of the 15th Battalion the HLI (City of Glasgow
Regiment),* Thomas Chalmers, John McCallum & Co., 1934. Nominal Roll Sep
1914–Nov 1915. (Glasgow, Mitchell Library)
*A Saga of Scotland. History of the 16th Battalion the HLI (City of Glasgow
Regiment),* Thomas Chalmers, John McCallum & Co., 1930. Nominal Roll.
(Glasgow, Mitchell Library)

The Seventeenth Highland Light Infantry (Glasgow Chamber of Commerce Battalion) Record of War Service 1914–18, David J. Clark, Glasgow, 1920. (H.L.I. Museum)

The Seaforth Highlanders, Colonel John M. Sym (Ed.), Gale & Polden Ltd., 1962.

History of the Fourth Battalion The Seaforth Highlanders, Lieutenant-Colonel M.M. Haldane, H.F.& G. Witherby, 1928. (Also covers Home Defence and Reserve Bns.)

War Diary of the Fifth Seaforth Highlanders 51st (Highland) Division, Captain D. Sutherland, John Lane, The Bodley Head, 1920.

6th Seaforth Highlanders. Campaign Reminiscences Captains R.T. Peel and A.H. MacDonald, W.R. Walker & Co., 1923.

The Gordon Highlanders in the First World War 1914–19, Cyril Falls, The University Press, 1958. (Volume 4 of the Life of a Regiment.)

With the Gordons at Ypres, Rev. A.M. Maclean, Alexander Gardner, 1916, (1st Bn.)

The Sixth Gordons in France and Flanders (with the 7th and 51st Div.), Captain D. Mackenzie, War Memorial Committee, Rosemount Press, 1921.

The 11th Battalion Gordon Highlanders 1914–16, Maclure, Macdonald & Co. Ltd., Glasgow, 1916.

Student under Arms. Being the War Adventures of the Aberdeen University Company of the Gordon Highlanders, Alexander Rule, The University Press, 1934.

Historical Records of the Cameron Highlanders 1908–31, Vols. III and V, the Regimental Historical Records Committee, William Blackwood & Sons, 1931. Includes all battalions in WWI.

The 79th News, The Journal of the Queen's Own Cameron Highlanders, Apr 1891–Sep 1960, Diary of the 4th Battalion, The Queen's Own Cameron Highlanders during the European War, Northern Chronicle, Inverness, 1916.

The Fifth Camerons, Captain J.H.F. McEwen MP, David Macdonald Ltd., 1938.

War History of the 6th (Service) Battalion Queen's Own Cameron Highlanders, Lieutenant-Colonel Norman MacLeod, Edinburgh, 1934.

The Sixth Cameron Highlanders Souvenir Book, WDR, Spottiswoode & Co. Ltd., 1916.

The History of the 7th Battalion Queen's Own Cameron Highlanders, Colonel J.W. Sandilands and Lieutenant-Colonel Norman Macleod, Eneas Mackay, 1922.

History of the Argyll and Sutherland Highlanders. 1st Battalion 1909–39, Brigadier R.C.B. Anderson, T.& A. Constable Ltd., 1954. (Stirling Central Library)

Am Reisimeid Chataich, The 93rd Sutherland, now 2nd Battalion, The Argyll and Sutherland Highlanders (Princess Louise's), 1799–1927, Brigadier-General A.E.J. Cavendish, Butler & Tanner Ltd., 1928.

The 10th Battalion Argyll and Sutherland Highlanders 1914–19, Lieutenant-Colonel H.G. Sotheby, John Murray, 1931.

The Sword of the North. Highland Memories of the Great War, Dugald Mac Echern, Robert Carruther & Sons, Courier Office, 1923. This book includes chapters on most Scottish Regiments including, The Lovat Scouts and Scottish Horse).

Youth of Yesteryear. Campaigns, Battles, Service and Exploits of the Glasgow Territorials in the last Great War, S. Munro, William Hodge & Co. Ltd., 1939.

The Proud Trooper. The History of the Ayrshire (Earl of Carrick's Own) Yeomanry from its Raising in the 18th Century till 1964, Major W.S. Brownlie, Collins, 1964.

The Fife and Forfar Yeomanry and 14th (F and F Yeomanry) Battalion Royal Highlanders 1914–19, Major D.D. Ogilvie, John Murray, 1921.

The Queen's Own Royal Glasgow Yeomanry, Robert Maclehose & Co.Ltd., 1949.

The Scottish Horse 1900–40, The Duchess of Atholl, Jackson Son & Co., 1940. (Copy in Museum)

History of the Scottish Horse 1900–56, Colonel Campbell Preston. (Museum)

Roll of Officers, 1st Dunbartonshire Volunteer Rifle Corps 1860–1908, etc., Lieutenant-Colonel F. Rorke (Ed.). With historical notes on several Regiments. Published for the TF Association of the County of Dunbarton, 1937.

The History of the Orkney and Shetland Volunteers and Territorials 1793–1958, D. Rollo, The Shetland Times, 1958, 37pp. (Orkney CRO)

Museums
Replies were received from the following Regiments.

The Royal Scots
The Castle, Edinburgh EH1 2YT.
No lists of men held; only War Diaries and printed books.

The Royal Scots Fusiliers
518 Sauchiehall St., Glasgow, G2 3LW.
Printed books.
Scrapbook of 2nd Bn. Royal Scots Fusiliers. 1914–18.
The Royal Scots Fusiliers Journal, published annually, Jan 1917–Jan 1920.
1st Bn. Orders for 1908.
No lists of men held.

The Cameronians (Scottish Rifles)
Mote Hill, off Muir Street, Hamilton, Lanarkshire ML3 6BY.

The Black Watch
Balhousie Castle, Perth PH1 5HS.
Printed books.
Records not disclosed but a list is held of those held at the National Register of Archives (Scotland), West Register House, Edinburgh EH2 4DF and at the Royal Commission for Historical Manuscripts, Quality Court, Chancery Lane, London WC2A 1HP (0171-242-1198).

The Highland Light Infantry
518 Sauchiehall St., Glasgow, G2 3LW.
Printed books.
HLI chronicle. Lists wounded, POWs, awards, of all Bns. Often includes a roll of men.
The Seaforth Highlanders
Fort George, Invernessshire IV1 2DD.
Roll of 2 Bn. 1914. (S57)
The Gordon Highlanders
RHQ, Viewfield Road, Aberdeen AB15 7XH.
No lists of men.
The Queen's Own (Cameron Highlanders)
Fort George, Invernessshire IV1 2DD.
Enlistment Books 1899–1931.
Printed books.
The Argyll and Sutherland Highlanders
The Castle, Stirling.
No lists of men held; only printed books, most of which refer to WWII.
The Scottish Horse
The Cross, Dunkeld, Perthshire.
Records from 1900 to 1940. No details given but does include wounded.
Printed books.
See also the Black Watch.
The Ayrshire Yeomanry
Rozelle House, Monument Road, Alloway by Ayr KA7 4NQ.
Many photographs, maps and documents.

Other museums
The Scottish United Services Museum
The Castle, Edinburgh EH1 2NG.
Has a library of 7000 volumes dealing with Scottish military history as well as many prints and documents which are available for students of military history.

Record Offices
Grampian Archives, Aberdeen
Roll of Service of Eddieston School, Peterculter Parish, Aberdeenshire.
Aberdeen and District POW Bureau 1915–18. (AC 9/4/1–5)
Ref. –/5 has a list of men.
Dumfries and Galloway, Buccleugh St., Dumfries
No lists of men held.
Orkneys, Laing St., Kirkwall
List of ex-service men from Kirkwall and St. Ola in Welcome Home pamphlet. (Ref. 941.09YZ)

Local newspapers. *The Orcadian* and *The Orkney Herald* have details of men.
Strathclyde, PO Box 27, Glasgow G2 1DU
Files on 1st and 2nd Bn. Highland Light Infantry. These include (D-TC 19.1/57):
Nominal Rolls for (garter) tabs.
Files on RFA and RE.
Scottish Central Archives, Spittal St., Stirling
Burgh of Alloa Roll of Honour.
Allan's School, Stirling Roll of Honour.
Dundee Archives
Holds many registers for applications for parochial relief for County of Angus.
1st City of Dundee Volunteer Drill Register 1917–18. (GD/Mus 69).
Forfar District Recruiting Tribunal: applications for exemptions 1916–18.
Angus County Records. (ACC/12/4A/1)
Scottish RO, H.M. New Register House, Edinburgh EH1 3YY
A source list of WWI documents is in preparation.
City of Dundee National Reserve. List of men by Coys. (MD7/3)
Edinburgh Branch Old Comtemptibles Association members list 1928. (GD1/770/1)
POWs. (GD50/184/112)
Box 16 Field Service Books and papers Section 16 RAMC. (GD232)
1st Bn. orders. Grenadier Guards. (GD364/1/48)
Wm. Crawford and Sons Ltd., Bakers, Edinburgh. Roll of Service. (GD381/1/12)
Macfarlane Lang and Co. Ltd., Baker, Glasgow. Roll of Service. (GD381/2/15)
Incorporation of Carters in Leith. Roll of Service. (GD399/195)
Moray RO, Forres
Not contacted.

Libraries
The following have been named as having records. They have not been contacted.
Perth and Kinross District Archives.
Sandeman Library, Perth.
Wm.Coull Anderson Library of Genealogy, Dewar House, Hill Terrace, Arbroath.
Hamilton District Museum (Museum for Cameronians, Scottish Rifles).
Dumfries, Ewart Library.
Aberdeen City Archives.
Aberdeen City Library.
Aberdeen University Library.
North East Scotland Library, 14 Crown St., Aberdeen.
Moray District Library, Elgin.
Dundee Central Library, Wellgate. Roll of Honour of Caxton House Printing Office,
    Dundee. James P. Mathew, 1920.
Dundee Local History Library. Printed books only.
Glasgow, The Mitchell Library. Printed books only.

Glasgow Local Collection. Has a list of Rolls of Honour which includes the following
Rolls of Service:
Bellahouston Academy.
Faculty of Procuration in Glasgow.
Glasgow Academy. (SOG and BL)
Glasgow High School 1st and 2nd editions.
George Watson's College, Edinburgh.
Edinburgh University.
Coatbridge and the Great War, S. Lindsay.
The Morayshire Roll of Honour, W.J. McKenzie
The Clan Macrae, Macrae.
Mull and Iona Association 1914–15.
Northern Assurance Co. Ltd.
The War Book of Turriff and 12 Miles Around, J.M. Robertson.
St. Andrews University 1914–19.
Glasgow University.
Graham (Wm.) and Co., Glasgow 1914–19.
Hillhead High School 1914–19.
Scottish Co-operative Wholesale Society Ltd.
Aberdeen University Roll of Honour.
Clarke and Co. Ltd., Paisley.
United Collieries Active Service Rolls 1914–19.
Stirling Central Library. Printed books.

Other records
Balquhidder Church, Perthshire has Roll of Service.
Draft History of Renfrewshire TF Association is in Cheshire CRO. (Acc 2332/5)
Arbroath. Roll of Honour, Arbroath and District, 1914–19, Arbroath, 1921, 243pp.
Liturgies, Church of Scotland. Order of Service at the Unveiling of the War
    Memorial in Cardross Parish Church, and Roll of Honour. 16pp. Helensburgh,
    1920.
Edinburgh. Royal High School 1914–18. Roll of Honour, 110pp. 1920 and 1922.
Edinburgh. University of Edinburgh. Roll of Honour, 1914–19. 786pp. 1921.
Greenock. Memorial Record of men of Greenock who fell in the Great War, 1914–18.
    1924.
Muster Roll of the Manse, D. Cameron. Names of Ministers of the Church of
    Scotland, and of members of their families, on active service or engaged in work
    connected with the War. Glasgow, 1919.
National Guardian Scottish Trade Roll of Honour. European War, 1914–15, published
    by National Trade Guardian, Glasgow, 1916.
Roll of Honour. St. George's-in-the-West Parish, Aberdeen, James Smith, Aberdeen.
    1915–17, 3pp.

Roll of Honour of soldiers and sailors connected with Boharm, S. Ree, Keith, 1915.
Denny. Denny and Dunipace Roll of Honour, 1914—18, Edinburgh, 1920, 115pp.
Dundee. Caxton House Printing Office. The Roll of Honour of Caxton House Printing Office, Dundee. A record of the employees who served in the war, Dundee, 1920, 340pp.
Hawick and the War. A Pictorial Record, Hawick, 1914—19, 228pp.
Loyal Lewis. Roll of Honour, 1914 and After, W. Grant, Stornoway, 1920, 343pp.
Roll of Honour of Nairnshire, T.R. Ramage, Nairn, 1915, 24pp. (9082.ff.15)
Nairn Parish Church, Roll of Honour, Nairn, 1914, 12pp.
Shetland's Roll of Honour and Roll of Service, T. Manson, Lerwick, 1920, 284pp.
City of Aberdeen Roll of Honour. A record of those belonging to Aberdeen and District who gave their lives for their country in the Great War. Aberdeen, 1926.
County of Kirkcudbright. The Stewartry Roll of Honour in the Great War, Castle-Douglas, 1927.
Saint John the Baptist Church at Perth. Perthshire War Memorial. Restoration of the Church of St. John, Perth, 1925, 20pp.
University of Aberdeen, Book of Remembrance, 1914—18; 1939—45, Aberdeen, 1952.
Glasgow. Clan Mackay Society. Clan Mackay Society War Memorial Volume, 1924, 56pp.
The Union Bank of Scotland Ltd. Roll of Honour, 1914—18, Glasgow, 1922.
Clan Donald. Clan Donald Roll of Honour, 1914—18, Glasgow 1931, 360pp.
Roll of Honour Dumbarton and Balloch Joint Line Railway. On Dumbarton Station and Dumbarton Library; all who served.
The Glasgow Evening Times, 1914—18 has many obituaries.

13

IRISH REGIMENTS

THE IRISH REGIMENTS

The Irish Guards, see Guards
The Royal Irish Regiment
The Royal Inniskilling Fusiliers
The Royal Irish Rifles
Princess Victoria's (Royal Irish Fusiliers)
The Connaught Rangers
The Prince of Wales's Leinster Regiment
   (Royal Canadians)
The Royal Munster Fusiliers
he Royal Dublin Fusiliers

For the following regiments, see the Cavalry section:

4th (Royal Irish) Dragoon Guards
5th Royal Irish Lancers
6th Inniskilling Dragoon
8th (Kings Royal Irish) Hussars
The North Irish Horse
The South Irish Horse

Books

The Campaigns and Histories of the Royal Irish Regiment, Vol. 2, 1910–22, Brigadier-General Stannus Geoghegen, Wm. Blackwood, 1927.
The Royal Inniskillings in the World War, Sir F. Fox, Constable, 1928.
With the 2nd Battalion The Royal Inniskilling Fusiliers in France 1914–16, Major C.A.M. Alexander, Ornagh-Tyrone Constitution, 1928. (Also 6th and 7th Service Bns. see A.S. White.)
The History of the 1st Seven Battalions of the Royal Irish Rifles in the Great War, Vol.II, Cyril Falls.
The Connaught Rangers, Lieutenant-Colonel H.F.N. Jourdain and E. Fraser.
The Irish Regiments in the First World War, Henry Harris, 1968.
The History of the 36th (Ulster) Division, Cyril Falls, 1922.

Museums
   Royal Irish Fusiliers
Drumadd Barracks, Armagh BFPO 803.
No lists of men held.
   Royal Irish Rifles
Royal Ulster Rifles Museum, Regimental HQ, 5 Waring Street, Belfast BT1 2EW.
14th Royal Irish Rifles. Nominal Roll 1915.
16th Royal Irish Rifles. Regimental Scrapbook 1914—18.
20th Royal Irish Rifles. Battalion Orders 1915—16.
No other museums located or contacted.
The Museum of the Irish Regiments is now at the National Army Museum.

14

CHANNEL ISLANDS

STATES OF JERSEY

States of Jersey Library Service
Book of Remembrance of Victoria College, Jersey, published by J.T. Bigwood, Jersey, 1920, 17 pp.
Island of Jersey. The Great War 1914–19, published by J.T. Bigwood, Jersey, 1919. Roll of Honour and Record of Service; includes names of 862 killed and 6,292 who served.